WeightWatchers®

MY TurnAround® PROGRAM COOKBOOK

A Word About Weight Watchers

Since 1963, Weight Watchers has grown from a handful of people to millions of enrollments annually. Today, Weight Watchers is recognized as the leading name in safe and sensible weight control. Weight Watchers members form diverse groups, from youths to senior citizens, attending meetings virtually around the globe. Weight-loss and weight-management results vary by individual, but we recommend that you attend Weight Watchers meetings to benefit from the supportive environment you'll find there and follow the comprehensive Weight Watchers program which includes food plans, an activity plan, and a thinking skills plan. For the Weight Watchers meeting nearest you, call **800-651-6000.** For information on bringing Weight Watchers to your workplace, call **800-8AT-WORK.** Also, visit us at our Web site, **WeightWatchers.com,** or look for ***Weight Watchers Magazine*** at your newsstand or in your meeting room.

Introduction

Are you ready to find success? With Weight Watchers **TurnAround**® you'll find a host of ideas for managing your weight, staying motivated, and feeling good about the changes you're making in your life.

To help you on your way to losing weight, we've developed *My TurnAround Program Cookbook,* a 200-recipe book just for you, covering every meal and every course, from starters, sandwiches, soups, salads, and savory side dishes to satisfying entrées and delectable desserts.

Inside, you'll find delicious recipes for our successful **Flex Plan** and **Core Plan**® plus directions for making many of our **Flex Plan** recipes fit the **Core Plan.** We also provide:

- Bookmarks to help you locate your favorite recipes
- A ***POINTS***® value recipe index and a **Core Plan** recipe index, which make it easy for you to find just what **you** need
- Tips for making many recipes even simpler
- Smart ideas for buying lean meats, nutritious fruits and vegetables, whole-grain foods, and low-fat dairy products
- Suggestions for making extra for a healthful brown-bag lunch or a good-for-you but indulgent snack
- Instructions for preparing and doubling recipes that freeze well so that you'll be prepared for those days when you're short on time
- Tips for keeping meals and snacks with low ***POINTS*** values on hand for the times you know will be a challenge

With *My TurnAround Program Cookbook* we provide scrumptious but simple everyday recipes that will help you make the wise food choices you'll need to reach **your** goal. We wish you success—and hope that you'll have fun—as you follow these recipes and tips in the spirit of **TurnAround.**

WEIGHT WATCHERS PUBLISHING GROUP

EDITORIAL DIRECTOR	**NANCY GAGLIARDI**
ART DIRECTOR	**ED MELNITSKY**
PRODUCTION MANAGER	**ALAN BIEDERMAN**
OFFICE MANAGER AND PUBLISHING ASSISTANT	**JENNY LABOY-BRACE**
FOOD EDITOR	**EILEEN RUNYAN**
EDITOR	**CAROL PRAGER**
RECIPE DEVELOPERS	**DAVID BONOM**
	JAIME HARDER
	MARK SCARBROUGH
	ALICE THOMPSON
	BRUCE WEINSTEIN
NUTRITION CONSULTANT	**PATTY SANTELLI**
PHOTOGRAPHER	**RITA MAAS**
FOOD STYLIST	**MICHAEL PEDERSON**
PROP STYLIST	**CATHY COOK**
DESIGN/PRODUCTION	**LYNDA D'AMICO**
COVER DESIGN	**DANIELA HRITCU**

ON THE COVER: Chicken Roasted Over Squash (***POINTS*** value: ***5***), page 113

 Editorial and art produced by W/W Twentyfirst Corp., 747 Third Ave., NY, NY 10017.

SKU #0011140 Printed in the USA

About Our Recipes

We make every effort to ensure that you will have success with our recipes. For best results and for nutritional accuracy, please keep the following guidelines in mind:

- Recipes in this book have been developed for Weight Watchers members who are following either the **Flex Plan** or the **Core Plan** on **TurnAround**. All **Core Plan** recipes are marked with our **Core Plan** icon ☑. We include ***POINTS*** values so you can use any of the recipes if you are following the **Flex Plan** on the program. ***POINTS*** values are assigned based on calories, fat (grams), and fiber (grams) provided for a serving size of a recipe.

- All recipes feature approximate nutritional information; our recipes are analyzed for Calories (Cal), Total Fat (Fat), Saturated Fat (Sat Fat), Trans Fat (Trans Fat), Cholesterol (Chol), Sodium (Sod), Carbohydrates (Carb), Dietary Fiber (Fib), Protein (Prot), and Calcium (Calc).

- Nutritional information for recipes that include meat, poultry, and fish are based on cooked skinless boneless portions (unless otherwise stated), with the fat trimmed.

- We recommend that you buy lean meat and poultry, then trim it of all visible fat before cooking. When poultry is cooked with the skin on, we suggest removing the skin before eating.

- We follow the USDA guidelines for cooking meats and poultry to safe temperatures to prevent foodborne illness, but for beef and lamb (steaks, roasts, and chops) be aware that cooking them to the recommended minimum of 145°F will give you a medium cooked steak, roast, or chop.

- Before serving, divide foods—including any vegetables, sauce, or accompaniments—into portions of equal size according to the designated number of servings per recipe.

- Any substitutions made to the ingredients will alter the "Per serving" nutritional information and may affect the **Core Plan** recipe status or the ***POINTS*** value.

- It is implied that all fresh fruits, vegetables, and greens in recipes should be rinsed before using.

MANGO SORBET, PAGE 294
AND CHOCOLATE CRANBERRY
BISCOTTI, PAGE 289

Contents

CHAPTER ONE

SMART STARTERS

AND SNACKS

Thai Beef on Lettuce Leaves

HANDS-ON PREP **20 MIN**
COOK **NONE**
SERVES **4**

- **3** tablespoons fresh lime juice
- **1** tablespoon sugar
- **2** teaspoons Asian fish sauce (nam pla)
- **1** teaspoon grated peeled fresh ginger
- **¼** teaspoon Thai red curry paste
- **¾** pound thinly sliced lean roast beef, cut into thin strips
- **1** carrot, grated
- **½** red bell pepper, seeded and thinly sliced
- **½** small red onion, thinly sliced
- **½** cucumber, peeled, seeded, and chopped
- **¼** cup chopped fresh cilantro
- **4** Boston lettuce leaves

1 Combine the lime juice, sugar, fish sauce, ginger, and curry paste in a small bowl; mix well to dissolve the sugar.
2 Combine the roast beef, carrot, bell pepper, red onion, cucumber, and cilantro in a large bowl. Add the lime juice mixture and toss well to combine.
3 To serve, place 1 lettuce leaf on each of 4 plates. Fill each lettuce leaf with ¾ cup of the beef mixture. Cut each filled leaf in half and serve at once.

PER SERVING (1 filled lettuce leaf): 134 Cal, 3 g Fat, 1 g Sat Fat, 0 g Trans Fat, 41 mg Chol, 1112 mg Sod, 10 g Carb, 1 g Fib, 18 g Prot, 24 mg Calc. ***POINTS*** value: ***3.***

GOOD IDEA If you prefer to skip the beef, this savory filling can be prepared with an equal amount of cooked shrimp, sea scallops, or skinless duck breast.

THAI BEEF ON LETTUCE LEAVES

SAUSAGE- AND HERB-STUFFED MUSHROOMS

Sausage- and Herb-Stuffed Mushrooms

HANDS-ON PREP **20 MIN**
COOK **35 MIN**
SERVES **6**

- **30** **medium fresh white mushrooms (about 1¼ pounds)**
- **½** **pound Italian turkey sausage, casings removed**
- **1** **small onion, finely chopped**
- **2** **garlic cloves, minced**
- **¼** **cup chopped fresh parsley**
- **¼** **cup Italian seasoned dried bread crumbs**
- **2** **tablespoons grated Parmesan cheese**
- **1** **egg white**
- **¼** **teaspoon salt**
- **⅛** **teaspoon freshly ground pepper**

1 Preheat the oven to 350°F. Spray a large rimmed baking sheet with nonstick spray.
2 Remove the stems from the mushrooms and finely chop. Set the chopped stems and the caps aside.
3 To make the filling, heat a medium nonstick skillet over medium-high heat. Add the sausage and cook, stirring to break it up into smaller pieces, until no longer pink, 2–3 minutes. Add the reserved mushroom stems, the onion, and garlic; cook, stirring occasionally, just until beginning to brown, 6–7 minutes. Transfer the mixture to a bowl and let cool 5 minutes. Stir in the parsley, bread crumbs, cheese, egg white, salt, and pepper; mix well. Stuff each mushroom cap with about 2½ teaspoons of the filling; place in a single layer on the baking sheet.
4 Bake until the mushroom caps are tender and browned, 25–30 minutes.

PER SERVING (5 stuffed mushrooms): 101 Cal, 3 g Fat, 1 g Sat Fat, 0 g Trans Fat, 24 mg Chol, 491 mg Sod, 9 g Carb, 2 g Fib, 11 g Prot, 45 mg Calc. ***POINTS*** value: ***2.***

EXPRESS LANE For healthy party food in a snap, stuff the mushrooms as directed through step 3; wrap well and freeze up to 2 weeks. The night before you want to serve them, let the mushrooms gradually thaw in the refrigerator. Bake as directed except increase the baking time by 5 to 10 minutes.

Smoked Salmon Cucumber Rolls

HANDS-ON PREP **20 MIN**
COOK **25 MIN**
SERVES **12**

- **1 cup short-grain white rice**
- **1¼ cups water**
- **1½ tablespoons seasoned rice vinegar**
- **2 teaspoons honey**
- **⅛ teaspoon salt**
- **4 (8 x 7-inch) sheets nori**
- **½–¾ teaspoon wasabi paste**
- **8 teaspoons light cream cheese (Neufchâtel)**
- **4 (1-ounce) slices smoked salmon, each cut lengthwise into 4 strips**
- **1 cucumber, peeled, seeded, and cut into 16 strips**
- **1 tablespoon pickled ginger, thinly sliced**
- **3 tablespoons reduced-sodium soy sauce**

1 Combine the rice and water in a medium saucepan; bring to a boil. Reduce the heat and simmer, covered, until the liquid evaporates, about 20 minutes. Remove the pan from the heat and let stand 10 minutes.

2 Meanwhile, combine the vinegar, honey, and salt in a small bowl. Stir the vinegar mixture into the rice until blended; let cool 10 minutes.

3 Place a bamboo rolling mat on a work surface so that the slats are horizontal. Place 1 nori sheet, shiny-side down, with one short side facing you, on the mat. Dampen hands with water and spread a slightly rounded ½ cup of the rice on the sheet leaving about a 1-inch border across the top. Spread ⅛ teaspoon of the wasabi crosswise along the center of the rice. Spread 2 teaspoons of the cream cheese on top of the wasabi. Top the wasabi and cream cheese with 4 strips of the salmon, then 4 strips of the cucumber.

4 Holding the filling in place with your fingers, gently roll the mat forward with your thumbs until the 2 edges of the nori overlap to form a 7-inch roll. Seal the roll with a few drops of water on the far edge of the nori.

5 Transfer the roll to a cutting board. With a very sharp knife moistened with water, cut the roll crosswise into 6 pieces. Repeat with the remaining nori, rice, wasabi, cream cheese, salmon, and cucumber to make 4 rolls. Top each piece with a little bit of the ginger and serve with the soy sauce.

PER SERVING (2 pieces with ¾ teaspoon soy sauce): 83 Cal, 2 g Fat, 1 g Sat Fat, 0 g Trans Fat, 7 mg Chol, 460 mg Sod, 12 g Carb, 1 g Fib, 4 g Prot, 11 mg Calc. ***POINTS*** value: ***2.***

Brazilian Shrimp Cocktail

HANDS-ON PREP **10 MIN**
COOK **20 MIN**
SERVES **4**

- **1 pound medium shrimp, peeled and deveined**
- **½ cup plain fat-free yogurt**
- **¼ cup minced red onion**
- **2 tablespoons chopped pimientos**
- **1 tablespoon tomato paste**
- **2 teaspoons grated horseradish in vinegar**
- **¼ teaspoon freshly ground pepper**
- **2 cups shredded iceberg lettuce**
- **4 lime wedges**

1 Bring a large pot of water to a boil. Add the shrimp and cook, stirring frequently, until just opaque in the center, about 3 minutes. Drain in a colander. Rinse the shrimp under cold running water; drain. Pat dry on paper towels and set aside.

2 Meanwhile, whisk together the yogurt, red onion, pimientos, tomato paste, horseradish, and pepper in a small bowl.

3 Arrange ½ cup of the lettuce on each of 4 plates. Evenly divide the shrimp into 4 portions and arrange on the lettuce. Top each with a scant ¼ cup of the sauce. Serve with the lime wedges.

PER SERVING (1 shrimp cocktail): 116 Cal, 1 g Fat, 0 g Sat Fat, 0 g Trans Fat, 169 mg Chol, 232 mg Sod, 7 g Carb, 2 g Fib, 20 g Prot, 89 mg Calc. ***POINTS*** value: ***2.***

GOOD IDEA Make this easier by using precooked shrimp instead of cooking it yourself. Also, if you keep a bag of frozen precooked shrimp in your freezer, you can make this treat at a moment's notice.

Shrimp and Potato Tapas

HANDS-ON PREP **15 MIN**
COOK **25 MIN**
SERVES **6**

- **1 pound red potatoes, scrubbed and cut into ½-inch pieces**
- **2 tablespoons olive oil**
- **1 pound medium shrimp, peeled, deveined, and halved lengthwise**
- **4 garlic cloves, minced**
- **1½ tablespoons white-wine vinegar**
- **½ teaspoon crushed red pepper**
- **½ teaspoon salt**

1 Combine the potatoes and enough water to cover in a large saucepan; bring to a boil. Cook until fork-tender, about 7 minutes. Drain in a colander and let cool 5 minutes.
2 Heat the oil in a large nonstick skillet over medium-high heat. Add the potatoes and cook, shaking the pan occasionally, until browned and crisp, about 5 minutes.
3 Add the shrimp and garlic; cook, stirring frequently, until the shrimp are just opaque in the center, about 2 minutes. Stir in the vinegar, crushed red pepper, and salt.

PER SERVING (½ cup): 159 Cal, 5 g Fat, 1 g Sat Fat, 0 g Trans Fat, 112 mg Chol, 329 mg Sod, 14 g Carb, 2 g Fib, 14 g Prot, 36 mg Calc. ***POINTS*** value: ***3.***

FOOD NOTE Like all traditional tapas from Spain, this dish can be served at once or cooled to room temperature and served later, if you like.

SHRIMP AND POTATO TAPAS

Pineapple Salsa

HANDS-ON PREP **15 MIN**
COOK **5 MIN**
SERVES **8**

1 poblano pepper
2 cups diced peeled and cored fresh pineapple
1 small red onion, minced
1 garlic clove, minced
2 tablespoons chopped fresh mint
1 tablespoon rice or white-wine vinegar
½ teaspoon salt

1 Hold the poblano over an open gas flame and roast, turning frequently, until blackened on all sides, about 3 minutes. Or preheat the broiler; place the poblano on a baking sheet and broil 5 inches from the heat, turning occasionally, until blackened on all sides, about 4 minutes. Place the poblano in a paper bag and fold closed, or place it in a small bowl and cover with plastic wrap. Let steam about 10 minutes.
2 Meanwhile, combine the pineapple, red onion, garlic, mint, vinegar, and salt in a medium bowl. When cool enough to handle, peel the poblano, discard the seeds, and chop. Add the poblano to the pineapple mixture; stir gently. Serve at once or store, covered, in the refrigerator up to 2 days.

PER SERVING (⅓ cup): 28 Cal, 0 g Fat, 0 g Sat Fat, 0 g Trans Fat, 0 mg Chol, 147 mg Sod, 7 g Carb, 1 g Fib, 1 g Prot, 9 mg Calc. ***POINTS*** value: ***0.***

TRY IT *Poblano* (poh-BLAH-noh) peppers are the familiar chile used in chili rellenos. They're a long, thin, green chile with a rich flavor and spiky heat. Dried, they turn red and become known as ancho chiles. These days, poblanos are available most of the year in the produce section of almost all supermarkets—but their official season runs from mid-summer to early fall.

Caribbean Mango Salsa

HANDS-ON PREP **15 MIN**

COOK **NONE**

SERVES **6**

- **2 large mangoes, peeled, pitted, and chopped**
- **1 yellow bell pepper, seeded and finely chopped**
- **1 shallot, minced**
- **1 jalapeño pepper, seeded and chopped (wear gloves to prevent irritation)**
- **1 tablespoon minced peeled fresh ginger**
- **2 teaspoons dry jerk seasoning**
- **2 teaspoons fresh lime juice**

Combine the mangoes, bell pepper, shallot, jalapeño, ginger, jerk seasoning, and lime juice in a medium bowl. Serve at once with cut up veggies. Or store, covered, in the refrigerator up to 3 days.

PER SERVING (½ cup): 55 Cal, 0 g Fat, 0 g Sat Fat, 0 g Trans Fat, 0 mg Chol, 169 mg Sod, 14 g Carb, 2 g Fib, 1 g Prot, 11 mg Calc. ***POINTS*** value: ***1.***

GOOD IDEA Spiff up your next serving of everyday grilled chicken or seafood with a side of this delicious, antioxidant-rich salsa.

FROM LEFT, CLOCKWISE: CARIBBEAN MANGO SALSA, PAGE 19; COWBOY CAVIAR; AND PINEAPPLE SALSA, PAGE 18

Cowboy Caviar

HANDS-ON PREP **15 MIN**
COOK **NONE**
SERVES **6**

- **1 (15-ounce) can black-eyed peas, rinsed and drained**
- **4 scallions, thinly sliced**
- **2 small shallots, sliced into thin rings**
- **1 green bell pepper, seeded and chopped**
- **1 celery stalk, thinly sliced**
- **1 plum tomato, chopped**
- **3 tablespoons apple-cider vinegar**
- **½ teaspoon cinnamon**
- **½ teaspoon dried marjoram, crumbled**
- **½ teaspoon dried thyme**
- **½ teaspoon salt**
- **¼ teaspoon freshly ground pepper**
- **2–4 dashes hot pepper sauce, or to taste**

Combine the black-eyed peas, scallions, shallots, bell pepper, celery, tomato, vinegar, cinnamon, marjoram, thyme, salt, ground pepper, and pepper sauce in a medium bowl; toss well. Serve at once or cover and refrigerate up to 4 days.

PER SERVING (½ cup): 79 Cal, 0 g Fat, 0 g Sat Fat, 0 g Trans Fat, 0 mg Chol, 370 mg Sod, 17 g Carb, 5 g Fib, 4 g Prot, 82 mg Calc. ***POINTS*** value: ***1.***

GOOD IDEA Keep a batch of this healthful Texas appetizer on hand to scoop into a celery "boat" or Belgian endive leaf as a satisfying snack. It's also a flavorful treat if friends drop in.

Guacamole

HANDS-ON PREP **10 MIN**
COOK **NONE**
SERVES **8**

- **2 ripe avocados, pitted and peeled**
- **1 medium shallot, minced**
- **1 (4½-ounce) can chopped hot, medium, or mild green chiles**
- **1 plum tomato, finely chopped**
- **1 tablespoon fresh lime juice**
- **¼ teaspoon salt**
- **¼ teaspoon freshly ground pepper**
- **3 dashes hot pepper sauce, or to taste**

Place the avocado flesh in a medium bowl; mash with a fork until creamy but still slightly chunky. Stir in the shallot, chiles, tomato, lime juice, salt, ground pepper, and pepper sauce. Serve at once or store, covered, in the refrigerator up to 2 hours.

PER SERVING (2 tablespoons): 91 Cal, 8 g Fat, 1 g Sat Fat, 0 g Trans Fat, 0 mg Chol, 93 mg Sod, 6 g Carb, 3 g Fib, 2 g Prot, 7 mg Calc. ***POINTS*** value: ***2.***

FOOD NOTE There are many theories about preventing guacamole from oxidizing and turning brown including the one about placing the avocado pit in the dip. But the only true fix is adding an acidic ingredient—as we did with the lime juice and tomato in this recipe. Ultimately, guacamole is best served immediately for best presentation and taste.

Moroccan Carrot Dip with Pita Triangles

HANDS-ON PREP **10 MIN**
COOK **30 MIN**
SERVES **6**

- **1** pound carrots, cut into 1-inch pieces
- **1** tablespoon extra-virgin olive oil
- **1** small garlic clove
- **1½** teaspoons fresh lemon juice
- **½** teaspoon ground cumin
- **½** teaspoon salt
- **¼ + ⅛** teaspoon cinnamon
- **¼** teaspoon ground coriander
- **¼** teaspoon ground ginger
- **⅛** teaspoon cayenne
- **1** teaspoon paprika (optional)
- **3** (6-inch) whole-wheat pita breads, cut into 8 wedges each

1 Bring a large saucepan of water to a boil. Add the carrots and cook until tender, 20–22 minutes; drain. Let cool 5 minutes.
2 Put the carrots, oil, garlic, lemon juice, cumin, salt, cinnamon, coriander, ginger, and cayenne in a food processor and process until smooth. Transfer to a serving bowl and sprinkle with paprika (if using). Serve warm or at room temperature with the pita wedges.

PER SERVING (¼ cup dip with 4 pita wedges): 142 Cal, 3 g Fat, 0 g Sat Fat, 0 g Trans Fat, 0 mg Chol, 403 mg Sod, 26 g Carb, 5 g Fib, 4 g Prot, 29 mg Calc. ***POINTS*** value: ***2.***

MAKE IT CORE Serve this flavorful dip with cut up veggies, such as broccoli and cauliflower florets, bell pepper strips, and small fresh mushrooms instead of the pita wedges.

Curried Edamame

HANDS-ON PREP **5 MIN**
COOK **15 MIN**
SERVES **6**

- **1 (1-pound) bag frozen unshelled edamame (green soybeans)**
- **2 teaspoons canola oil**
- **1 teaspoon Asian (dark) sesame oil**
- **1 teaspoon curry powder**
- **½ teaspoon ground coriander**
- **½ teaspoon salt**

1 Bring a large pot of water to a boil. Add the edamame and cook until bright green, about 5 minutes; drain.
2 Heat the canola and sesame oil in a large nonstick skillet over medium-high heat. Add the curry powder and coriander; cook until fragrant, about 30 seconds. Add the edamame and cook, stirring constantly, until hot and well coated, about 1 minute. Sprinkle with the salt and serve at once.

PER SERVING (about ¼ cup): 123 Cal, 5 g Fat, 0 g Sat Fat, 0 g Trans Fat, 0 mg Chol, 224 mg Sod, 9 g Carb, 4 g Fib, 8 g Prot, 53 mg Calc. ***POINTS*** value: ***2.***

ZAP IT Buy an extra bag of edamame at the supermarket or Asian grocery store and stash it in the freezer. Just zap it in the microwave according to package directions for a nutritious, anytime snack.

Sautéed Artichoke Hearts with Garlic and Lemon

HANDS-ON PREP **10 MIN**
COOK **5 MIN**
SERVES **6**

- **1 tablespoon extra-virgin olive oil**
- **2 (14-ounce) cans artichoke hearts, drained and quartered**
- **⅛ teaspoon crushed red pepper**
- **3 garlic cloves, thinly sliced**
- **½ teaspoon salt**
- **1 lemon, cut into 6 wedges**

Heat the oil in a large nonstick skillet over medium-high heat. Add the artichokes and crushed red pepper; cook, stirring occasionally, until artichokes just start to brown, about 4 minutes. Stir in the garlic and salt; cook, stirring occasionally, until the garlic is golden, 2–3 minutes. Serve with the lemon wedges.

PER SERVING (scant ½ cup with 1 lemon wedge): 60 Cal, 2 g Fat, 0 g Sat Fat, 0 g Trans Fat, 0 mg Chol, 431 mg Sod, 7 g Carb, 0 g Fib, 3 g Prot, 6 mg Calc. ***POINTS*** value: ***1.***

HOW WE DID IT Pat the canned artichokes dry with paper towels before sautéing them—this will allow them to brown, rather than steam, in the pan.

Vegetable Shu Mai

HANDS-ON PREP **25 MIN**
COOK **25 MIN**
SERVES **8**

DIPPING SAUCE

- **¼ cup reduced-sodium soy sauce**
- **1 small scallion, chopped**
- **1 tablespoon honey**
- **2 teaspoons fresh lemon juice**
- **1 teaspoon grated peeled fresh ginger**

SHU MAI

- **2 teaspoons Asian (dark) sesame oil**
- **1 tablespoon grated peeled fresh ginger**
- **2½ cups shredded napa cabbage**
- **1 small onion, chopped**
- **¼ pound fresh shiitake mushrooms, stems removed and caps chopped**
- **1 carrot, shredded**
- **2 tablespoons hoisin sauce**
- **24 (3-inch) wonton skins**

1 To make the dipping sauce, combine the all the ingredients and set aside.
2 To make the shu mai, heat the sesame oil in a large nonstick skillet over medium-high heat. Add the ginger and cook, stirring constantly, just until fragrant, about 30 seconds. Add the cabbage, onion, and mushrooms; cook, stirring frequently, until softened, 4–5 minutes. Add the carrot and cook, stirring occasionally, until vegetables are cooked through, 3–4 minutes. Add the hoisin sauce and cook, stirring constantly, until fragrant, about 30 seconds. Remove the skillet from the heat and cool 10 minutes.
3 Arrange 6 of the wonton skins on a work surface. Place 1½ teaspoons of the filling in the center of each skin. One at a time, pleat the edge of the skin up and around the filling, pressing to seal. Repeat with the remaining wonton skins and filling to make 24 shu mai.
4 Spray a steamer basket with nonstick spray and arrange 12 of the shu mai in the basket. Set the basket in a saucepan over 1 inch of boiling water. Cover tightly and steam the shu mai until cooked through, 5–6 minutes. Transfer the shu mai to a serving tray and keep warm. Repeat with the remaining 12 shu mai. Serve at once with the dipping sauce.

PER SERVING (3 shu mai with about 2 scant teaspoons dipping sauce): 117 Cal, 2 g Fat, 0 g Sat Fat, 0 g Trans Fat, 2 mg Chol, 513 mg Sod, 22 g Carb, 1 g Fib, 4 g Prot, 36 mg Calc. ***POINTS*** value: **2.**

VEGETABLE SHU MAI

Roasted Plum Tomatoes with Fresh Basil

HANDS-ON PREP **10 MIN**
COOK **40 MIN**
SERVES **6**

- **6 plum tomatoes (about 1¼ pounds), cored and halved lengthwise**
- **2 teaspoons extra-virgin olive oil**
- **1 teaspoon dried oregano**
- **½ teaspoon salt**
- **⅛ teaspoon freshly ground pepper**
- **12 fresh basil leaves**

1 Preheat the oven to 375°F. Spray a shallow baking pan with olive oil nonstick spray.
2 Combine the tomatoes, oil, oregano, salt, and pepper in a bowl; toss well. Arrange the tomatoes, cut-side up, in the baking pan. Roast until the tomatoes are tender and the skins wrinkle, 38–40 minutes. Transfer to a serving platter and top each tomato half with a basil leaf.

PER SERVING (2 tomato halves): 27 Cal, 2 g Fat, 0 g Sat Fat, 0 g Trans Fat, 0 mg Chol, 200 mg Sod, 3 g Carb, 1 g Fib, 1 g Prot, 9 mg Calc. ***POINTS*** value: ***1.***

GOOD IDEA Roast a double batch of tomatoes and set aside half to toss into salads, layer in a sandwich, or combine with pasta later in the week. Simply store the roasted tomatoes in an airtight container in the refrigerator up to 3 days.

Southwestern Popcorn

HANDS-ON PREP **10 MIN**
COOK **NONE**
SERVES **6**

6 cups air-popped popcorn
1 tablespoon chili powder
½ teaspoon paprika
½ teaspoon cinnamon
½ teaspoon ground cumin

Place the popcorn in a large bowl; lightly spray with canola nonstick spray and toss. Lightly spray with canola nonstick spray again, then sprinkle the spices over the popcorn. Toss, then serve at once or store in zip-close plastic bags up to 1 month.

PER SERVING (1 cup): 36 Cal, 1 g Fat, 0 g Sat Fat, 0 g Trans Fat, 0 mg Chol, 14 mg Sod, 7 g Carb, 2 g Fib, 1 g Prot, 9 mg Calc. ***POINTS*** value: ***0.***

GOOD IDEA For a touch of nutritious sweetness and a burst of energy, stir ¾ cup raisins into the mix and deduct it from your **weekly *POINTS* Allowance** (2 tablespoons raisins per serving will increase the ***POINTS*** value by 1).

CHAPTER TWO

EVERYDAY

SALADS

ROAST BEEF PANZANELLA SALAD

Roast Beef Panzanella Salad

HANDS-ON PREP **15 MIN**
COOK **NONE**
SERVES **4**

- **6** **ounces day-old whole-wheat ciabatta or French bread, cut into 1-inch cubes**
- **2** **large ripe tomatoes, coarsely chopped**
- **⅓** **English cucumber, chopped**
- **1** **small red onion, chopped**
- **3** **tablespoons balsamic vinegar**
- **1** **tablespoon extra-virgin olive oil**
- **¼** **cup chopped fresh mint or basil**
- **1** **tablespoon drained capers**
- **½** **teaspoon salt**
- **¼** **teaspoon freshly ground pepper**
- **½** **pound thinly sliced lean roast beef, cut into strips**

1 Combine the ciabatta, tomatoes, cucumber, red onion, vinegar, oil, mint, capers, salt, and pepper in a large bowl. Toss well and let stand until the bread soaks up the juices, about 20 minutes.
2 Stir in the roast beef and serve at once.

PER SERVING (1½ cups): 246 Cal, 8 g Fat, 2 g Sat Fat, 0 g Trans Fat, 27 mg Chol, 1,191 mg Sod, 30 g Carb, 5 g Fib, 17 g Prot, 53 mg Calc. ***POINTS*** value: ***5.***

FOOD NOTE We make this traditional Italian bread salad with crusty whole-wheat bread, plenty of veggies, and a minimum of oil. Tasty strips of roast beef make it a complete meal, but you could substitute lean cooked pork or chicken, or even a can of rinsed and drained kidney beans.

Zesty Beef Salad

HANDS-ON PREP **15 MIN**
COOK **10 MIN**
SERVES **4**

- **1 pound boneless sirloin steak, trimmed**
- **2 tablespoons chili powder**
- **½ cup prepared taco sauce**
- **1 tablespoon Worcestershire sauce**
- **½ teaspoon mustard powder**
- **1 (15-ounce) can hearts of palm, rinsed, drained, and thinly sliced**
- **1 small jicama, peeled and cut into matchstick-thin strips**
- **1 red bell pepper, seeded and thinly sliced**
- **2 cups bean, radish, or garlic sprouts**
- **2 tablespoons chopped fresh chives**

1 Spray the broiler rack with canola nonstick spray and preheat the broiler.
2 Rub both sides of the steak with the chili powder; place on the broiler rack. Broil the steak 5 inches from the heat until an instant-read thermometer inserted in the center of the steak registers 145°F for medium, about 5 minutes on each side. Transfer the steak to a cutting board; let stand about 5 minutes.
3 Meanwhile, whisk together the taco sauce, Worcestershire sauce, and mustard powder in a small bowl. Place the hearts of palm, jicama, bell pepper, and sprouts in a serving bowl. Add the taco sauce mixture and toss to coat.
4 Cut the steak on an angle against the grain into 12 slices and place on top of the salad. Sprinkle with the chives and serve.

PER SERVING (1¼ cups salad with 3 slices steak): 255 Cal, 7 g Fat, 2 g Sat Fat, 0 g Trans Fat, 64 mg Chol, 438 mg Sod, 21 g Carb, 9 g Fib, 27 g Prot, 87 mg Calc. ***POINTS*** value: ***5.***

GOOD IDEA Whenever you see a recipe calling for bell peppers, choose red, orange, or yellow over green—they are much sweeter and richer in antioxidants.

Chicken and Pasta Salad with Cucumber-Ranch Dressing

HANDS-ON PREP **15 MIN**

COOK **20 MIN**

SERVES **6**

- **1** cup peeled, seeded, and diced cucumber
- **½** cup fat-free mayonnaise
- **¼** cup low-fat buttermilk
- **3** tablespoons chopped fresh chives
- **1** tablespoon fresh lemon juice
- **1** teaspoon Dijon mustard
- **¼** teaspoon celery seeds
- **¼** teaspoon salt
- **½** pound farfalle
- **1** pound skinless boneless chicken breasts, lightly pounded
- **1** bunch watercress, tough stems discarded and chopped
- **1** cup grape or cherry tomatoes, halved
- **3** scallions, finely chopped

1 To make the dressing, puree ½ cup of the cucumber, the mayonnaise, buttermilk, chives, lemon juice, mustard, celery seeds, and salt in a blender or food processor; set aside.

2 Cook the pasta according to package directions omitting the salt, if desired; drain. Rinse under cold running water; drain and transfer to a large bowl.

3 Meanwhile, spray a large nonstick skillet with nonstick spray and set over medium-high heat. Add the chicken and cook until cooked through, about 4 minutes on each side. Transfer the chicken to a cutting board, let cool 5 minutes, then thinly slice on the diagonal.

4 Add the chicken to the pasta. Stir in the watercress, tomatoes, scallions, and the remaining ½ cup cucumber. Add the dressing and toss well to coat. Serve at once.

PER SERVING (1½ cups): 270 Cal, 4 g Fat, 1 g Sat Fat, 0 g Trans Fat, 46 mg Chol, 490 mg Sod, 36 g Carb, 2 g Fib, 23 g Prot, 64 mg Calc. ***POINTS*** value: ***5.***

MAKE IT CORE Use fat-free buttermilk instead of the low-fat version and choose whole-wheat farfalle or another medium-size, whole-wheat pasta, such as penne or ziti.

Greek Chicken Salad with Creamy Feta Dressing

HANDS-ON PREP **15 MIN**
COOK **10 MIN**
SERVES **6**

6 **tablespoons fat-free mayonnaise**
¼ **cup crumbled fat-free feta cheese**
2 **tablespoons fat-free sour cream**
1 **tablespoon fat-free milk**
2 **teaspoons grated lemon zest**
2 **teaspoons fresh lemon juice**
1 **garlic clove, minced**
1 **pound skinless boneless chicken breasts, lightly pounded**
1 **teaspoon dried oregano**
4 **cups torn romaine lettuce leaves**
1 **tomato, chopped**
1 **green bell pepper, seeded and chopped**
½ **cucumber, peeled, seeded, and diced**
½ **red onion, finely chopped**
12 **black olives, pitted and coarsely chopped**

1 To make the dressing, combine the mayonnaise, cheese, sour cream, milk, lemon zest, lemon juice, and garlic in a small bowl. Cover and refrigerate until ready to serve.
2 Sprinkle the chicken with the oregano. Spray a large nonstick skillet with canola nonstick spray and set over medium-high heat. Add the chicken and cook until cooked through, about 4 minutes on each side. Transfer the chicken to a cutting board, let stand about 5 minutes, then thinly slice on the diagonal.
3 Combine the lettuce, tomato, bell pepper, cucumber, red onion, and olives in a large bowl. Divide the lettuce mixture among 6 serving bowls. Top the salad evenly with the chicken and drizzle with the dressing. Serve at once.

Per serving (1½ cups salad with about 4 slices chicken and 3 tablespoons dressing): 143 Cal, 4 g Fat, 1 g Sat Fat, 0 g Trans Fat, 43 mg Chol, 321 mg Sod, 9 g Carb, 2 g Fib, 18 g Prot, 63 mg Calc. ***POINTS*** value: ***3.***

HOW WE DID IT Lightly pounding the chicken breasts makes the chicken less dense and gives you thinner (and consequently more) slices. Just place a chicken breast between two sheets of plastic wrap or wax paper and lightly pound with a meat mallet or heavy saucepan.

Chicken and Spinach Salad with Curry Vinaigrette

HANDS-ON PREP **5 MIN**

COOK **10 MIN**

SERVES **4**

1 tablespoon curry powder

1 pound skinless boneless chicken breasts, cut into ¾-inch pieces

2 tablespoons red-wine vinegar

1 tablespoon extra-virgin olive oil

½ teaspoon freshly ground pepper

¼ teaspoon salt

1 (6-ounce) bag washed baby spinach leaves

¼ pound fresh mushrooms, quartered

½ red onion, thinly sliced

1 Place the curry powder in a small dry skillet over low heat and cook, stirring frequently, until fragrant, about 1 minute. Immediately transfer the curry powder to a plate and let cool.

2 Spray a medium nonstick skillet with olive oil nonstick spray and set over medium-high heat. Add the chicken and cook, turning occasionally, until cooked through, about 8 minutes.

3 Meanwhile, combine the vinegar, curry powder, oil, pepper, and salt in a large bowl. Add the chicken, spinach, mushrooms, and red onion; toss to coat. Serve at once.

PER SERVING (generous 2 cups): 187 Cal, 6 g Fat, 1 g Sat Fat, 0 g Trans Fat, 63 mg Chol, 271 mg Sod, 8 g Carb, 3 g Fib, 25 g Prot, 54 mg Calc. ***POINTS*** value: ***4.***

FOOD NOTE If you crave a touch of sweetness and crunch in this recipe, add ¼ cup dried currants with the chicken in step 2, then sprinkle the salad with 2 tablespoons toasted pine nuts. Following the **Core Plan**? Increase the per-serving ***POINTS*** value by 1, and deduct it from your **weekly *POINTS* Allowance.**

Cashew Chicken and Broccoli Salad

HANDS-ON PREP **15 MIN**
COOK **10 MIN**
SERVES **4**

- **2** tablespoons seasoned rice vinegar
- **1** tablespoon reduced-sodium soy sauce
- **1** tablespoon mirin
- **1** teaspoon minced peeled fresh ginger
- **1** teaspoon Asian (dark) sesame oil
- **¼** teaspoon crushed red pepper
- **¾** pound skinless boneless chicken breasts, cut into 1-inch pieces
- **3** cups coarsely chopped fresh broccoli
- **1** red bell pepper, seeded and thinly sliced
- **½** cup chopped fresh cilantro
- **¼** cup shredded carrot
- **2** scallions, finely chopped
- **¼** cup coarsely chopped unsalted cashews

1 To make the dressing, whisk together the vinegar, soy sauce, mirin, ginger, sesame oil, and crushed red pepper in a small bowl until blended; set aside.

2 Spray a large nonstick skillet with nonstick spray and set over medium-high heat. Add the chicken and cook, turning occasionally, until cooked through, about 8 minutes.

3 Combine the broccoli, bell pepper, cilantro, carrot, and scallions in a large bowl; add the dressing and toss well to coat.

4 Add the chicken to the broccoli mixture and toss lightly. Divide the salad among 4 plates and serve sprinkled with the cashews.

PER SERVING (1½ cups salad with 1 tablespoon cashews): 209 Cal, 8 g Fat, 2 g Sat Fat, 0 g Trans Fat, 51 mg Chol, 208 mg Sod, 11 g Carb, 4 g Fib, 23 g Prot, 65 mg Calc. ***POINTS*** value: ***4.***

TRY IT *Mirin* (MIHR-in), a sweet Japanese rice wine used for cooking, is available in Japanese markets and the gourmet section of large supermarkets. You may substitute sweet white wine or apple juice.

CASHEW CHICKEN AND
BROCCOLI SALAD

Chinese Chicken and Noodle Salad

HANDS-ON PREP **15 MIN**
COOK **10 MIN**
SERVES **4**

- **2** tablespoons seasoned rice vinegar
- **1** tablespoon reduced-sodium soy sauce
- **1** tablespoon reduced-fat peanut butter
- **1** tablespoon packed brown sugar
- **1** teaspoon Asian (dark) sesame oil
- **1** teaspoon minced peeled fresh ginger
- **1** garlic clove, minced
- **½** pound chicken tenders
- **¼** pound rice stick noodles
- **½** cup fresh sugar-snap peas, trimmed and cut diagonally in half
- **½** cucumber, peeled, seeded, and cut into thin strips
- **½** red bell pepper, seeded and thinly sliced
- **½** cup chopped fresh cilantro
- **¼** cup unsalted dry-roasted peanuts, coarsely chopped

1 To make the dressing, whisk together the vinegar, soy sauce, peanut butter, brown sugar, sesame oil, ginger, and garlic in a medium bowl until blended; set aside.

2 Spray a large nonstick skillet with nonstick spray and set over medium-high heat. Add the chicken and cook, turning occasionally, until cooked through, about 8 minutes. Transfer the chicken to a cutting board; let stand about 5 minutes. With your fingers or two forks, tear the chicken into shreds; set aside.

3 Meanwhile, place the noodles in a large bowl and add enough hot water to cover; let the noodles stand until soft, about 10 minutes. Drain the noodles in a colander and transfer to a large bowl of cold water to cool. Drain again, then place in a large bowl. Add the chicken, sugar-snap peas, cucumber, bell pepper, and cilantro. Drizzle with the dressing and toss well to coat. Serve, sprinkled with the peanuts.

Per serving (1 cup salad with 1 tablespoon peanuts): 286 Cal, 9 g Fat, 2 g Sat Fat, 0 g Trans Fat, 34 mg Chol, 210 mg Sod, 33 g Carb, 3 g Fib, 17 g Prot, 35 mg Calc. ***POINTS*** value: ***6.***

EXPRESS LANE Turn this salad into a quick, no-cook meal by using deli-roasted chicken—you'll need about 1 cup of shredded cooked chicken.

Buffalo Chicken Salad with Creamy Blue Cheese Dressing

HANDS-ON PREP **15 MIN**

COOK **10 MIN**

SERVES **4**

- **¼ cup + 1 tablespoon fat-free mayonnaise**
- **¼ cup fat-free sour cream**
- **3 tablespoons crumbled blue cheese**
- **1 teaspoon apple-cider vinegar**
- **¾ cup cornflake crumbs**
- **1 pound chicken tenders**
- **2 tablespoons jarred buffalo wing sauce**
- **6 cups torn iceberg lettuce leaves**
- **1 tomato, chopped**
- **1 carrot, cut into matchstick-thin strips**
- **1 small red onion, finely chopped**

1 Preheat the oven to 450°F. Spray a small baking pan with nonstick spray.

2 To make the dressing, combine the ¼ cup mayonnaise, the sour cream, cheese, and vinegar in a small bowl; set aside.

3 Place the cornflake crumbs on a sheet of wax paper.

4 Combine the chicken, buffalo wing sauce, and the 1 tablespoon mayonnaise in a medium bowl. Dip the chicken, 1 piece at a time, into the crumbs. Place the chicken in the baking pan in one layer. Lightly spray with nonstick spray. Bake, turning once, until the chicken is cooked through, about 10 minutes. Transfer the chicken to a cutting board and cut into 1-inch pieces.

5 Combine the lettuce, tomato, carrot, and red onion in a large bowl. Add the dressing and toss to coat. Top with the chicken and serve at once.

PER SERVING (2 cups): 267 Cal, 7 g Fat, 2 g Sat Fat, 0 g Trans Fat, 74 mg Chol, 519 mg Sod, 22 g Carb, 3 g Fib, 29 g Prot, 106 mg Calc. ***POINTS*** value: ***5.***

GOOD IDEA You might like to double this dressing, which makes a tasty dip for vegetables. It can be made ahead and kept refrigerated up to 3 days.

GARDEN CHICKEN SALAD

Garden Chicken Salad

HANDS-ON PREP **15 MIN**
COOK **NONE**
SERVES **4**

- **1½** cups cubed cooked chicken
- **1** cup fresh sugar-snap peas, trimmed
- **1** cup grape tomatoes, halved
- **1** yellow bell pepper, seeded and diced
- **¼** cup chopped fresh chives
- **3** tablespoons white-wine vinegar
- **3** teaspoons extra-virgin olive oil
- **¼** teaspoon salt
- **1** (15-ounce) can whole beets, drained and quartered
- **2** tablespoons crumbled reduced-fat goat cheese

1 Combine the chicken, sugar-snap peas, tomatoes, bell pepper, chives, 2 tablespoons of the vinegar, 2 teaspoons of the oil, and the salt in a large bowl.
2 Toss the beets with the remaining 1 tablespoon vinegar and 1 teaspoon oil in a medium bowl.
3 Arrange the chicken mixture on a large platter; surround with the beets and sprinkle with the cheese.

PER SERVING (1¼ cups): 186 Cal, 8 g Fat, 2 g Sat Fat, 0 g Trans Fat, 47 mg Chol, 367 mg Sod, 12 g Carb, 3 g Fib, 17 g Prot, 41 mg Calc. ***POINTS*** value: ***4.***

MAKE IT CORE Substitute any fat-free cheese (such as fat-free feta, cheddar, or mozzarella) for the reduced-fat goat cheese.

Turkey Sausage and White Bean Salad

HANDS-ON PREP **15 MIN**

COOK **15 MIN**

SERVES **6**

- **2** tablespoons red-wine vinegar
- **3** teaspoons olive oil
- **2** teaspoons whole-grain Dijon mustard
- **1** garlic clove, minced
- **¼** teaspoon salt
- **1** pound hot Italian turkey sausage, cut diagonally into 2-inch pieces
- **4** cups mixed salad greens, coarsely chopped
- **1** (15½-ounce) can cannellini (white kidney) beans, rinsed and drained
- **1** green bell pepper, seeded and diced
- **½** red onion, finely chopped
- **2** tablespoons chopped pimientos

1 To make the dressing, whisk together the vinegar, 2 teaspoons of the oil, the mustard, garlic, and salt in a small bowl until blended; set aside.

2 Heat the remaining 1 teaspoon oil in a large nonstick skillet over medium-high heat. Add the sausage and cook, turning occasionally, until browned and cooked through, about 15 minutes.

3 Transfer the sausage to a large bowl. Add the salad greens, beans, bell pepper, red onion, and pimientos. Drizzle with the dressing and toss well to coat. Serve at once.

PER SERVING (scant 1 cup): 243 Cal, 12 g Fat, 3 g Sat Fat, 0 g Trans Fat, 44 mg Chol, 747 mg Sod, 17 g Carb, 5 g Fib, 18 g Prot, 47 mg Calc. ***POINTS*** value: ***5.***

FOOD NOTE Turkey sausage is a delicious lower-fat substitute for pork sausage. We choose hot turkey sausage for this dish, but use mild turkey sausage if your family doesn't like spicy food.

Tuna, Bean, and Olive Salad

HANDS-ON PREP **15 MIN**
COOK **NONE**
SERVES **4**

- **2 (6-ounce) cans solid white tuna in water, drained and flaked**
- **1 (15½-ounce) can white navy beans, rinsed and drained**
- **1 red bell pepper, seeded and diced**
- **1 small onion, chopped**
- **¼ cup chopped pitted brine-cured kalamata olives**
- **¼ cup chopped flat-leaf parsley**
- **1 tablespoon chopped fresh oregano, or 1 teaspoon dried**
- **1 tablespoon balsamic vinegar**
- **1 garlic clove, minced**
- **¼ teaspoon freshly ground pepper**
- **4 Boston or Bibb lettuce leaves**

1 Combine the tuna, beans, bell pepper, onion, olives, parsley, oregano, vinegar, garlic, and ground pepper in a large bowl.
2 Arrange the lettuce cups on each of 4 plates; spoon the tuna mixture evenly into the cups and serve at once.

Per serving (1 lettuce leaf with 1 cup tuna salad): 214 Cal, 5 g Fat, 1 g Sat Fat, 0 g Trans Fat, 30 mg Chol, 599 mg Sod, 20 g Carb, 5 g Fib, 23 g Prot, 67 mg Calc. ***POINTS*** value: ***4.***

GOOD IDEA Prepare the tuna mixture the night before (the flavors will develop nicely), pack into containers, and refrigerate up to 1 day for a nutritious lunch.

Thai Shrimp and Noodle Salad

HANDS-ON PREP **10 MIN**
COOK **20 MIN**
SERVES **4**

- **4 cups water**
- **4 ounces rice noodles or whole-wheat linguine**
- **¼ pound fresh snow peas, trimmed**
- **2 cups shredded carrots**
- **6 scallions, chopped**
- **¼ cup chopped fresh basil**
- **¼ cup rice vinegar**
- **3 tablespoons Asian fish sauce (nam pla)**
- **2 garlic cloves, minced**
- **1 teaspoon sugar**
- **¼ teaspoon crushed red pepper**
- **1 pound cooked peeled and deveined large shrimp**
- **2 tablespoons chopped unsalted peanuts or 1 tablespoon sesame seeds**

1 Bring the water to a boil in a large pot. Add the noodles and snow peas; remove the pot from the heat. Cover and let the noodles stand according to directions until soft, but still slightly firm, about 6 minutes. Drain the noodles and snow peas in a colander and rinse under cold running water; drain again.

2 Meanwhile, combine the carrots, scallions, basil, vinegar, fish sauce, garlic, sugar, and crushed red pepper in a large bowl. Add the shrimp and the noodles and snow peas; toss well. Serve at once, sprinkled with the peanuts.

PER SERVING (1¾ cups): 292 Cal, 4 g Fat, 1 g Sat Fat, 0 g Trans Fat, 221 mg Chol, 1,324 mg Sod, 35 g Carb, 3 g Fib, 29 g Prot, 104 mg Calc. ***POINTS*** value: ***6.***

TRY IT Rice noodles can be found in the ethnic section of most supermarkets and in Asian markets, but you can substitute linguine if you like (just add the snow peas during the last minute of cooking).

Crab, Corn, and Black Bean Salad

HANDS-ON PREP **20 MIN**
COOK **5 MIN**
SERVES **6**

- **2** corn-on-the-cob, husked
- **1** pound cooked fresh or thawed frozen lump crabmeat, picked over
- **1** (15-ounce) can black beans, rinsed and drained
- **3** medium scallions, thinly sliced
- **1** red bell pepper, seeded and chopped
- **¼** cup fresh lemon juice
- **½** teaspoon celery seeds
- **¼** teaspoon salt
- **¼** teaspoon freshly ground pepper
- **2–3** dashes hot pepper sauce, or to taste

1 Spray the broiler rack with canola nonstick spray and preheat the broiler.
2 Broil the corn 5 inches from the heat, turning frequently, until lightly browned, about 3 minutes. Let the corn cool slightly, about 5 minutes. Cut the kernels off the cobs.
3 Combine the corn kernels and the remaining ingredients in a large bowl. Serve at once or cover and refrigerate up to 2 days.

PER SERVING (1 cup): 183 Cal, 6 g Fat, 1 g Sat Fat, 0 g Trans Fat, 71 mg Chol, 394 mg Sod, 15 g Carb, 4 g Fib, 18 g Prot, 101 mg Calc. ***POINTS*** value: ***3.***

GOOD IDEA If you have the grill going, grill extra corn-on-the-cob for tasty salads like this. To cut the corn kernels off the cobs, cut off the bottom end of each cob. Stand one corn-on-the-cob on its bottom on a cutting board, holding the cob near the top. With a large knife parallel to the cob, cut the kernels off with a sawing motion. Keep any extra corn kernels in the freezer to add nutritious fiber to stir-fries and salads.

Southwest Bean and Corn Salad

HANDS-ON PREP **15 MIN**
COOK **NONE**
SERVES **4**

- **1 tablespoon apple-cider vinegar**
- **1 tablespoon fresh lime juice**
- **1 tablespoon extra-virgin olive oil**
- **1 tablespoon chipotle chili powder**
- **¼ teaspoon salt**
- **¼ teaspoon coarsely ground black pepper**
- **1 (15½-ounce) can black beans, rinsed and drained**
- **1½ cups fresh or frozen corn kernels**
- **1 tomato, chopped**
- **½ red onion, finely chopped**
- **½ cup chopped fresh cilantro**

1 To make the dressing, whisk together the vinegar, lime juice, oil, chili powder, salt, and pepper in a bowl until blended; set aside.
2 Combine the beans, corn, tomato, red onion, and cilantro in a large bowl. Drizzle with the dressing and toss well to coat.

PER SERVING (about 1 cup): 163 Cal, 5 g Fat, 1 g Sat Fat, 0 g Trans Fat, 0 mg Chol, 308 mg Sod, 25 g Carb, 7 g Fib, 7 g Prot, 37 mg Calc. ***POINTS*** value: ***3.***

TRY IT Popular in Mexican cooking, *chipotle* (chih-POHT-lay) chili powder is actually made from dried jalapeños. It provides a distinctive warm heat and a delicious smoky flavor in this easy salad.

Tabbouleh with Olives and Mint

HANDS-ON PREP **15 MIN**
COOK **5 MIN**
SERVES **4**

- **1 cup bulgur**
- **1 cup boiling water**
- **1 tomato, chopped**
- **½ cucumber, peeled, seeded, and diced**
- **½ cup chopped fresh mint**
- **¼ cup chopped flat-leaf parsley**
- **2 scallions, finely chopped**
- **10 brine-cured kalamata olives, pitted and chopped**
- **1 tablespoon fresh lemon juice**
- **1 tablespoon extra-virgin olive oil**
- **½ teaspoon freshly ground pepper**
- **⅛ teaspoon salt**
- **⅓ cup crumbled fat-free feta cheese**

1 Place the bulgur in a large bowl. Pour the boiling water over the bulgur and let stand until the water is absorbed, about 30 minutes.
2 Add the tomato, cucumber, mint, parsley, scallions, olives, lemon juice, oil, pepper, and salt to the bulgur; toss well to coat. Sprinkle with the cheese.

PER SERVING (about ½ cup): 213 Cal, 7 g Fat, 1 g Sat Fat, 0 g Trans Fat, 0 mg Chol, 470 mg Sod, 33 g Carb, 8 g Fib, 9 g Prot, 106 mg Calc. ***POINTS*** value: ***4.***

GOOD IDEA Double the recipe, cover, and refrigerate the remaining half up to 3 days. It makes a great light lunch on a bed of mesclun or side dish with grilled chicken (3 ounces cooked skinless boneless chicken breast for each serving will increase the ***POINTS*** value by 3).

WARM PASTA E FAGIOLI SALAD

Warm Pasta e Fagioli Salad

HANDS-ON PREP **15 MIN**
COOK **20 MIN**
SERVES **4**

- **½ pound whole-wheat penne**
- **2 (15½-ounce) cans cannellini (white kidney) beans, rinsed and drained**
- **½ fennel bulb or 2 celery stalks, thinly sliced**
- **1 pint grape tomatoes, halved**
- **1 small onion, chopped**
- **2 garlic cloves, minced**
- **3–4 tablespoons white balsamic vinegar**
- **1 tablespoon extra-virgin olive oil**
- **¾ teaspoon salt**
- **½ teaspoon freshly ground pepper**
- **1 bunch watercress, tough stems discarded**
- **¼ cup sliced fresh basil**

1 Cook the pasta according to package directions omitting the salt, if desired.
2 Meanwhile, combine the beans, fennel, tomatoes, onion, garlic, vinegar, oil, salt, and pepper in a large bowl.
3 Drain the pasta and add to the bean mixture; toss well. Arrange the watercress on a platter, spoon the bean mixture on top, sprinkle with the basil, and serve at once.

PER SERVING (1¾ cups): 388 Cal, 5 g Fat, 1 g Sat Fat, 0 g Trans Fat, 0 mg Chol, 641 mg Sod, 73 g Carb, 13 g Fib, 16 g Prot, 117 mg Calc. ***POINTS*** value: ***7.***

HOW WE DID IT To slice fresh basil, stack 8 to 10 basil leaves on top of one another and roll up from one short end. Cut the roll into thin slices.

South American Tossed Salad

HANDS-ON PREP **15 MIN**
COOK **NONE**
SERVES **6**

- **1 small head Bibb lettuce, cleaned and torn**
- **4 large romaine lettuce leaves, torn**
- **2 tomatoes, chopped**
- **1 Hass avocado, pitted, peeled, and chopped**
- **6 radishes, thinly sliced**
- **1 cup fresh or frozen corn kernels**
- **¼ cup fresh lime juice**
- **4 teaspoons walnut oil**
- **½ teaspoon salt**
- **½ teaspoon freshly ground pepper**

Combine the lettuces, tomatoes, avocado, radishes, and corn in a large serving bowl. Sprinkle the salad with the lime juice, walnut oil, salt, and pepper and toss to coat. Serve at once.

PER SERVING (generous 1 cup): 130 Cal, 9 g Fat, 1 g Sat Fat, 0 g Trans Fat, 0 mg Chol, 119 mg Sod, 14 g Carb, 5 g Fib, 3 g Prot, 20 mg Calc. ***POINTS*** value: ***3.***

MAKE IT CORE Use flaxseed oil instead of walnut oil. Both are highly perishable, so once opened, store in the refrigerator up to 3 months.

Classic Caesar Salad

HANDS-ON PREP **10 MIN**
COOK **NONE**
SERVES **4**

¾ teaspoon anchovy paste
1 garlic clove, minced
1 tablespoon fresh lemon juice
1 teaspoon Dijon mustard
Dash Worcestershire sauce
2 tablespoons light mayonnaise
1 small head romaine lettuce, torn (about 8 cups)
2 tablespoons shredded Romano or Parmesan cheese
12 whole-wheat croutons

1 Mash the anchovy paste and garlic with a wooden spoon in a large wooden salad bowl. Stir in the lemon juice, mustard, and Worcestershire sauce until well combined. Stir in the mayonnaise.
2 Add the lettuce and toss to combine. Sprinkle with the cheese and croutons and serve at once.

PER SERVING (2 cups): 72 Cal, 4 g Fat, 1 g Sat Fat, 0 g Trans Fat, 5 mg Chol, 314 mg Sod, 7 g Carb, 2 g Fib, 4 g Prot, 88 mg Calc. ***POINTS*** value: ***1.***

TRY IT Anchovy paste is a puree of anchovies combined with vinegar and spices. It comes in tubes, making it convenient to use in sauces, dips, and dressings. Because anchovy paste is salty, use it sparingly. It will keep in the refrigerator up to 3 months. If you don't care for the taste of anchovies, you can substitute ¼ teaspoon salt.

Spring Greens with Radishes, Blue Cheese, and Toasted Walnuts

HANDS-ON PREP **10 MIN**
COOK **NONE**
SERVES **4**

- ½ **teaspoon grated lemon zest**
- 1½ **tablespoons fresh lemon juice**
- 2 **teaspoons extra-virgin olive oil**
- ¾ **teaspoon sugar**
- ¼ **teaspoon mustard powder**
- 2 **tablespoons finely chopped shallot**
- 1 **(7-ounce) bag mixed spring greens**
- 4 **radishes, thinly sliced**
- 1 **(1-ounce) piece blue cheese, frozen**
- 2 **tablespoons walnut pieces, toasted**

1 Combine the lemon zest, lemon juice, oil, sugar, and mustard powder in a salad bowl; mix well. Stir in the shallot. Add the spring greens and radishes; toss to coat.

2 Grate the frozen cheese onto the salad. Sprinkle with the walnuts and serve at once.

PER SERVING (about 1¼ cups): 88 Cal, 7 g Fat, 2 g Sat Fat, 0 g Trans Fat, 6 mg Chol, 111 mg Sod, 5 g Carb, 2 g Fib, 3 g Prot, 73 mg Calc. ***POINTS*** value: ***2.***

HOW WE DID IT Freeze the blue cheese—you'll find it easier to grate when frozen: Place the 1-ounce piece of cheese in the freezer at least 1 hour. Then grate the cheese using the medium-size holes on a four-sided grater.

SPRING GREENS WITH RADISHES, BLUE CHEESE, AND TOASTED WALNUTS

Japanese Salad with Sesame-Ginger Dressing

HANDS-ON PREP **10 MIN**
COOK **NONE**
SERVES **6**

- **2** tablespoons rice-wine vinegar
- **2** tablespoons reduced-sodium soy sauce
- **1** tablespoon Asian (dark) sesame oil
- **1** tablespoon grated peeled fresh ginger
- **4** teaspoons white or black sesame seeds
- **½** teaspoon sugar
- **1** garlic clove, minced
- Pinch cayenne
- **1** small head romaine lettuce, chopped (about 9 cups)

1 Combine the vinegar, soy sauce, sesame oil, ginger, sesame seeds, sugar, garlic, and cayenne in a medium bowl; mix well.

2 Divide the lettuce among 6 salad bowls. Spoon the dressing evenly on top (about 1 tablespoon per bowl) and serve at once.

PER SERVING (1 salad): 37 Cal, 2 g Fat, 0 g Sat Fat, 0 g Trans Fat, 0 mg Chol, 209 mg Sod, 3 g Carb, 2 g Fib, 2 g Prot, 34 mg Calc. ***POINTS*** value: ***1.***

GOOD IDEA Seeds and nuts can turn rancid quickly if stored on the pantry shelf. A better solution is to store them in the freezer, where they will stay fresh and ready to use for several months.

Arugula and Orange Salad with Toasted Pine Nuts

HANDS-ON PREP **10 MIN**
COOK **NONE**
SERVES **4**

- **2 tablespoons rice vinegar**
- **1 tablespoon orange juice**
- **1 teaspoon Asian (dark) sesame oil**
- **1 teaspoon honey**
- **1 teaspoon Dijon mustard**
- **1 teaspoon soy sauce**
- **1 (6-ounce) bag baby arugula**
- **1 navel orange, peeled and cut into sections**
- **4 thin slices red onion, halved**
- **2 tablespoons toasted pine nuts**

Whisk together the vinegar, orange juice, sesame oil, honey, mustard, and soy sauce in a large bowl until blended. Add the arugula, orange, and red onion; toss to coat. Sprinkle with the pine nuts and serve at once.

PER SERVING (1 ½ cups): 76 Cal, 4 g Fat, 1 g Sat Fat, 0 g Trans Fat, 0 mg Chol, 121 mg Sod, 9 g Carb, 2 g Fib, 3 g Prot, 88 mg Calc. ***POINTS*** value: ***1.***

GOOD IDEA Prepare twice as much of this tangy Asian dressing so you'll have some to drizzle over another salad later in the week. The dressing will keep in the refrigerator up to 3 days.

BOSTON LETTUCE STACKS WITH GOAT CHEESE, CRANBERRIES, AND PECANS

Boston Lettuce Stacks with Goat Cheese, Cranberries, and Pecans

HANDS-ON PREP **10 MIN**

COOK **NONE**

SERVES **4**

- 2 tablespoons raspberry vinegar
- 2 teaspoons extra-virgin olive oil
- ½ teaspoon sugar
- ¼ teaspoon salt
- ⅛ teaspoon freshly ground pepper
- 1 tablespoon finely chopped red onion
- 1 head Boston or Bibb lettuce, separated into leaves (about 16 leaves)
- 2 tablespoons dried cranberries
- 2 tablespoons crumbled goat cheese
- 2 tablespoons chopped toasted pecans

1 Combine the vinegar, oil, sugar, salt, and pepper in a small bowl; mix well. Stir in the red onion.

2 Cut the core from the center of the lettuce leaves so they will lie flat. Stack 4 leaves on each of 4 plates. Drizzle evenly with the dressing then sprinkle with the cranberries, cheese, and pecans and serve at once.

Per serving (1 salad): 90 Cal, 7 g Fat, 2 g Sat Fat, 0 g Trans Fat, 6 mg Chol, 184 mg Sod, 6 g Carb, 1 g Fib, 2 g Prot, 38 mg Calc. ***POINTS*** value: ***2.***

FOOD NOTE For this delicate dressing we like Boston or Bibb lettuce (sometimes called butterhead or butter lettuce because of their soft, buttery-textured leaves). Handle their tender leaves gently to avoid bruising.

Broccoli Waldorf Salad

HANDS-ON PREP **10 MIN**
COOK **NONE**
SERVES **4**

- **2 cups chopped fresh broccoli**
- **1 apple, chopped**
- **2 tablespoons raisins**
- **2 tablespoons low-fat mayonnaise**
- **1 tablespoon white balsamic vinegar**
- **2 tablespoons chopped toasted walnuts**

Combine the broccoli, apple, raisins, mayonnaise, and vinegar in a medium bowl; toss to coat. Serve at once or cover and refrigerate until ready to serve. Sprinkle with the walnuts just before serving.

PER SERVING (3/4 cup): 85 Cal, 3 g Fat, 0 g Sat Fat, 0 g Trans Fat, 0 mg Chol, 82 mg Sod, 14 g Carb, 3 g Fib, 2 g Prot, 26 mg Calc. ***POINTS*** value: ***1.***

GOOD IDEA Mix a double batch of this salad; it will keep in the refrigerator, covered, up to 2 days and makes a great side to a packed sandwich for lunch.

Indian Cucumber-Yogurt Salad

HANDS-ON PREP **10 MIN**
COOK **NONE**
SERVES **4**

- **½ cup plain fat-free Greek-style yogurt**
- **2 tablespoons chopped fresh mint**
- **¾ teaspoon ground cumin**
- **½ teaspoon salt**
- **⅛ teaspoon ground coriander**
- **⅛ teaspoon cayenne**
- **½ English cucumber, quartered lengthwise, then sliced**

Combine the yogurt, mint, cumin, salt, coriander, and cayenne in a medium bowl. Add the cucumber and mix well. Serve at once or cover and refrigerate up to 4 days.

PER SERVING (½ cup): 22 Cal, 0 g Fat, 0 g Sat Fat, 0 g Trans Fat, 0 mg Chol, 303 mg Sod, 2 g Carb, 1 g Fib, 3 g Prot, 28 mg Calc. ***POINTS*** value: ***0.***

TRY IT This chunky salad, often called *raita* (RI-tah) and found on the menu in many Indian restaurants, makes a refreshing side to fiery chili dishes as well as Indian entrées.

Malaysian Coleslaw with Toasted Sesame Seeds

HANDS-ON PREP **15 MIN**

COOK **NONE**

SERVES **6**

- **2** tablespoons rice vinegar
- **2** tablespoons Asian fish sauce (nam pla)
- **2** tablespoons chopped fresh cilantro
- **1** tablespoon minced peeled fresh ginger
- **2** scallions, finely chopped
- **1** tablespoon honey
- **2** teaspoons Asian (dark) sesame oil
- **1** garlic clove, minced
- **5** cups shredded napa cabbage
- **½** English cucumber, chopped
- **1** red bell pepper, seeded and diced
- **2** tablespoons toasted sesame seeds

1 Combine the vinegar, fish sauce, cilantro, ginger, scallions, honey, sesame oil, and garlic in a large bowl.

2 Add the cabbage, cucumber, and bell pepper; toss well. Serve at once or refrigerate, covered, up to 2 days. Sprinkle with the sesame seeds just before serving.

PER SERVING (generous 1 cup): 64 Cal, 3 g Fat, 0 g Sat Fat, 0 g Trans Fat, 0 mg Chol, 474 mg Sod, 9 g Carb, 2 g Fib, 2 g Prot, 62 mg Calc. ***POINTS*** value: ***1.***

TRY IT Asian sesame oil, also called dark sesame oil, can be found in the ethnic section of most supermarkets. It differs from regular sesame oil in that it has a deeper, nuttier flavor because it is made from toasted sesame seeds.

MALAYSIAN COLESLAW WITH TOASTED SESAME SEEDS

CHAPTER THREE

SATISFYING

SOUPS

SHREDDED BEEF AND POTATO SOUP WITH CHIMICHURRI

Shredded Beef and Potato Soup with Chimichurri

HANDS-ON PREP **15 MIN**
COOK **1 HR 25 MIN**
SERVES **6**

- **1 pound boneless bottom round steak, trimmed and cut into 1½-inch pieces**
- **½ teaspoon salt**
- **3 cups reduced-sodium beef broth**
- **1 (14½-ounce) can diced tomatoes with jalapeños**
- **⅓ cup chopped fresh cilantro or parsley**
- **2 tablespoons fresh lime juice**
- **1 garlic clove, minced**
- **¼ teaspoon crushed red pepper**
- **1 teaspoon olive oil**
- **1 onion, chopped**
- **2 celery stalks, chopped**
- **¼ teaspoon ground cloves**
- **2 cups (from a 24-ounce bag) precut diced potatoes**

1 Spray a large nonstick saucepan with olive oil nonstick spray and set over medium-high heat. Add the beef, in one layer, and sprinkle with ¼ teaspoon of the salt. Cook the beef, turning occasionally with tongs, until lightly browned, about 5 minutes. Add the broth and tomatoes; bring to a boil. Reduce the heat and simmer until the beef is fork-tender, about 1 hour.

2 With a slotted spoon, transfer the beef to a cutting board; let cool. Reserve the cooking liquid. With two forks, shred the beef into small pieces.

3 Meanwhile, to make the chimichurri, combine the cilantro, lime juice, garlic, the remaining ¼ teaspoon salt, and the crushed red pepper in a small bowl; set aside.

4 Heat the oil in a nonstick Dutch oven over medium heat. Add the onion and celery; cook, stirring occasionally, until softened, about 3 minutes. Add the cloves and cook, stirring constantly, until fragrant, about 1 minute. Add the potatoes and the reserved beef cooking liquid; bring to a boil. Reduce the heat and simmer until the potatoes are tender, about 10 minutes. Add the beef and simmer until heated through, about 2 minutes. Serve with the chimichurri.

PER SERVING (1 cup soup with 1 tablespoon chimichurri): 215 Cal, 8 g Fat, 3 g Sat Fat, 0 g Trans Fat, 46 mg Chol, 877 mg Sod, 18 g Carb, 2 g Fib, 17 g Prot, 44 mg Calc. ***POINTS*** value: ***5.***

GOOD IDEA Chimichurri, a classic Latin American condiment of cilantro, lime, and seasonings, can easily be doubled—refrigerate extras in an airtight container up to 3 days. Serve as a refreshing sidekick for grilled steak, pork chops, or burgers.

Hearty Caribbean Pork and Rice Soup

HANDS-ON PREP **15 MIN**
COOK **1 HR**
SERVES **4**

- **¾ pound pork tenderloin, trimmed and cut into ½-inch pieces**
- **2 teaspoons ground cumin**
- **1 teaspoon ground coriander**
- **2 teaspoons olive oil**
- **1 onion, chopped**
- **2 ounces Canadian bacon, diced**
- **2 garlic cloves, minced**
- **1–2 jalapeño peppers, seeded and finely chopped (wear gloves to prevent irritation)**
- **½ cup brown rice**
- **4 cups reduced-sodium chicken broth**
- **1 (14½-ounce) can diced tomatoes**
- **1 (10-ounce) package frozen mixed vegetables**
- **⅓ cup chopped fresh cilantro**

1 Sprinkle the pork with the cumin and coriander. Heat the oil in a nonstick Dutch oven over medium-high heat. Add the pork and cook, turning occasionally, until browned, about 5 minutes. Transfer the pork to a plate.

2 Add the onion, bacon, garlic, and jalapeño to the Dutch oven. Reduce the heat and cook, stirring frequently, until softened, about 3 minutes. Add the rice and cook, stirring constantly, until lightly toasted, about 1 minute. Return the pork to the pot, then add the broth and tomatoes. Bring to a boil, stirring to scrape up the browned bits from the bottom of the Dutch oven. Reduce the heat and simmer, covered, until the flavors are blended, about 35 minutes. Add the mixed vegetables and cook until the pork and vegetables are tender and the rice is cooked through, about 10 minutes. Stir in the cilantro and serve at once.

PER SERVING (1¾ cups): 327 Cal, 7 g Fat, 2 g Sat Fat, 0 g Trans Fat, 53 mg Chol, 964 mg Sod, 38 g Carb, 7 g Fib, 28 g Prot, 70 mg Calc. ***POINTS*** value: ***6.***

GOOD IDEA If you like, serve this one-pot meal with a warm small whole-wheat or pumpernickel roll and deduct it from your **weekly *POINTS* Allowance** (a 1-ounce roll will increase the ***POINTS*** value by 2).

Quick Pea Soup with Potatoes and Ham

HANDS-ON PREP **15 MIN**

COOK **20 MIN**

SERVES ***6***

- **1 (16-ounce) bag frozen peas, thawed**
- **1 (14½-ounce) can reduced-sodium chicken broth + enough water to equal 3 cups**
- **1 (14½-ounce) can sliced potatoes, rinsed and drained**
- **1 (14½-ounce) can sliced carrots, rinsed and drained**
- **¾ pound reduced-sodium lean ham, diced**
- **Freshly ground pepper, to taste**

1 Puree the peas and 1½ cups of the broth mixture in a blender; transfer to a large saucepan.

2 Stir in the remaining 1½ cups broth mixture, the potatoes, carrots, and ham; bring to a boil. Reduce the heat and simmer until the flavors are blended, about 5 minutes. Serve with pepper.

PER SERVING (1⅓ cups): 185 Cal, 4 g Fat, 1 g Sat Fat, 0 g Trans Fat, 30 mg Chol, 1,033 mg Sod, 21 g Carb, 5 g Fib, 18 g Prot, 35 mg Calc. ***POINTS*** value: ***3.***

FOOD NOTE If you are concerned with your salt/sodium intake, be aware that ham can be high in sodium. Take our cue and use reduced-sodium ham and canned broths. Rinsing canned vegetables also cuts some of the sodium.

Chicken Soup with Rice and Vegetables

HANDS-ON PREP **15 MIN**
COOK **1 HR**
SERVES **6**

- **1** slice thick-cut bacon, chopped
- **1** large onion, chopped
- **2** carrots, chopped
- **3** garlic cloves, minced
- **6** cups reduced-sodium chicken broth
- **1** (14½-ounce) can diced tomatoes
- **1** (1¼-pound) bone-in chicken breast, skinned and cut crosswise in half
- **½** cup long-grain white rice
- **3** cups chopped fresh broccoli
- **2** tablespoons shredded Parmesan cheese
- Freshly ground pepper, to taste

1 Spray a nonstick soup pot or large Dutch oven with nonstick spray and set over medium-high heat. Add the bacon, onion, carrots, and garlic; cook, stirring frequently, until lightly browned and softened, about 10 minutes.

2 Add the broth, tomatoes, chicken, and rice; bring to a boil. Reduce the heat and simmer, covered, until the chicken is cooked through and the rice is tender, about 40 minutes.

3 Lift the chicken from the soup and set aside until cool enough to handle. Pull the chicken from the bones, then tear or cut into bite-size pieces.

4 Meanwhile, add the broccoli to the soup; return to a boil. Reduce the heat and simmer, covered, until the broccoli is tender, about 6 minutes. Return the chicken to the pot and heat through. Serve the soup sprinkled with the cheese and pepper.

PER SERVING (scant 2 cups soup with 1 teaspoon cheese): 262 Cal, 7 g Fat, 2 g Sat Fat, 0 g Trans Fat, 46 mg Chol, 711 mg Sod, 24 g Carb, 3 g Fib, 25 g Prot, 105 mg Calc. ***POINTS*** value: ***5.***

GOOD IDEA Double the recipe and freeze half up to 3 months. You can reheat the soup with a little extra broth if necessary and enjoy this comforting favorite another time.

Easy Lentil-Chicken Soup

HANDS-ON PREP **15 MIN**
COOK **20 MIN**
SERVES **6**

- **2 teaspoons olive oil**
- **1 large zucchini, diced (about 2 cups)**
- **4 scallions, sliced**
- **2 (15-ounce) cans lentils, drained**
- **2 cups reduced-sodium chicken broth**
- **1 (14½-ounce) can Italian plum tomatoes**
- **2 cups shredded cooked chicken**
- **2 teaspoons fresh lemon juice**
- **1 tablespoon chopped fresh oregano, or 1 teaspoon dried**
- **½ teaspoon salt**
- **¼ teaspoon freshly ground pepper**
- **2 tablespoons grated Parmesan cheese**

1 Heat the oil in a Dutch oven or large saucepan over medium-high heat. Add the zucchini and scallions; cook, stirring occasionally, until softened, about 6 minutes. Add the lentils, broth, and tomatoes; bring to a boil, stirring to break up the tomatoes with a spoon. Add the chicken; reduce the heat and simmer until the flavors are blended, about 8 minutes.
2 Stir the lemon juice, oregano, salt, and pepper into the soup. Serve, sprinkled with the cheese.

PER SERVING (scant 1⅓ cups soup with 1 teaspoon cheese): 257 Cal, 6 g Fat, 2 g Sat Fat, 0 g Trans Fat, 42 mg Chol, 769 mg Sod, 25 g Carb, 9 g Fib, 26 g Prot, 95 mg Calc. ***POINTS*** value: ***5.***

MAKE IT CORE Sprinkle the soup with 2 or 3 tablespoons chopped fresh parsley or 1 tablespoon chopped fresh oregano instead of Parmesan cheese.

Vichyssoise with Poached Chicken and Watercress

HANDS-ON PREP **15 MIN**
COOK **40 MIN**
SERVES **8**

1 tablespoon canola oil
1 large leek, trimmed to white and light-green parts, cleaned, and sliced (about 4 cups)
7 cups reduced-sodium chicken broth
1½ pounds baking potatoes, peeled and cut into 1-inch pieces
2 carrots, cut into ½-inch pieces
1 teaspoon salt
¼ teaspoon ground mace or nutmeg
½ pound skinless boneless chicken breast
1 bunch watercress, tough stems discarded and chopped
1 cup fat-free half-and-half
Freshly ground pepper, to taste

1 Heat the oil in a nonstick Dutch oven over medium-high heat. Add the leek and cook, stirring occasionally, until lightly browned, 8–10 minutes. Add 2 cups of the broth, the potatoes, carrots, salt, and mace; bring to a boil. Reduce the heat and simmer, covered, until the vegetables are tender, about 15 minutes. Remove the pot from the heat and let cool 5 minutes.

2 Meanwhile, bring 2 cups of the broth to a boil in a medium saucepan. Add the chicken; reduce the heat and simmer, covered, until the chicken is just cooked through, about 10 minutes. Lift the chicken from the broth and let cool slightly. Set aside the broth. Cut the chicken into thin, diagonal slices; cover and refrigerate.

3 Pour the vegetable mixture into a blender or food processor and puree, in batches if necessary. Transfer the mixture to a large bowl. Stir in the remaining 3 cups broth plus the reserved broth; let the mixture cool to room temperature. Stir in the chicken, watercress, and half-and-half; refrigerate, covered, until chilled, about 2 hours. Season the soup with pepper just before serving.

PER SERVING (1½ cups): 192 Cal, 4 g Fat, 1 g Sat Fat, 0 g Trans Fat, 17 mg Chol, 759 mg Sod, 25 g Carb, 3 g Fib, 13 g Prot, 112 mg Calc. ***POINTS*** value: ***4.***

FOOD NOTE Cold potato soups like this French classic are terrific if you like to prepare your meals in advance. This recipe can be refrigerated up to 2 days. While cooked potatoes can be frozen, they tend to become watery upon reheating, so refrigeration versus freezing is preferable for keeping this soup tasting its best.

Paella Chowder

HANDS-ON PREP **20 MIN**
COOK **35 MIN**
SERVES **4**

- **2** teaspoons olive oil
- **1** large onion, chopped
- **2** garlic cloves, minced
- **½** cup long-grain white rice
- **1** teaspoon paprika
- **3** cups fish or vegetable broth, or 3 (8-ounce) bottles clam juice
- **1** (14½-ounce) can diced tomatoes
- **¾** teaspoon dried thyme
- **½** teaspoon saffron threads or turmeric
- **1** pound large shrimp, peeled and deveined
- **1** cup frozen peas
- **1** cup diced cooked chicken
- **1** tablespoon chopped, pitted manzanilla olives
- **¼** cup chopped fresh parsley
- Freshly ground pepper, to taste

1 Heat the oil in a nonstick Dutch oven over medium-high heat. Add the onion and garlic; cook, stirring frequently, until softened, about 3 minutes. Add the rice and paprika; cook, stirring frequently, until the rice is lightly toasted, about 2 minutes.

2 Add the broth, tomatoes, thyme, and saffron; bring to a boil. Reduce the heat and simmer, covered, until the rice is tender, about 18 minutes.

3 Add the shrimp and peas; return to a boil. Reduce the heat and simmer, covered, until the shrimp are barely opaque in the center, about 3 minutes. Add the chicken and olives; simmer until heated through, about 2 minutes. Stir in the parsley and pepper and serve at once.

PER SERVING (generous 2 cups): 308 Cal, 8 g Fat, 2 g Sat Fat, 0 g Trans Fat, 196 mg Chol, 713 mg Sod, 24 g Carb, 5 g Fib, 35 g Prot, 93 mg Calc. ***POINTS*** value: ***6.***

MAKE IT CORE Use ¾ cup quick-cooking brown rice instead of the white rice and simmer the mixture in step 2 only about 10 minutes.

FISH BALL SOUP VERACRUZ

Fish Ball Soup Veracruz

HANDS-ON PREP **25 MIN**
COOK **50 MIN**
SERVES **4**

- **2 teaspoons olive oil**
- **1 large onion, chopped**
- **1 poblano pepper, seeded and chopped (wear gloves to prevent irritation)**
- **3 garlic cloves, minced**
- **4 (8-ounce) bottles clam juice or 4 cups reduced-sodium vegetable broth**
- **1 (14½-ounce) can stewed tomatoes (no salt added)**
- **⅓ cup long-grain white rice**
- **1 pound sea scallops, patted dry**
- **¼ cup all-purpose flour**
- **1 large egg, lightly beaten**
- **¼ teaspoon ground anise or fennel seeds**
- **⅓ cup chopped fresh cilantro**
- **1 teaspoon grated orange zest**

1 Heat the oil in a nonstick Dutch oven over medium-high heat. Add the onion, poblano, and garlic; cook, stirring frequently, until lightly browned, about 7 minutes. Transfer half of the onion mixture to a food processor or blender; set aside.
2 Add the clam juice, tomatoes, and rice to the Dutch oven; bring to a boil. Reduce the heat and simmer, covered, until the rice is tender, about 20 minutes.
3 Meanwhile, add the scallops, flour, egg, and anise to the reserved onion mixture in the food processor and pulse just until chunky-smooth (do not puree). Transfer the scallop mixture to a bowl; cover and refrigerate until chilled, about 20 minutes.
4 Drop the scallop mixture by the tablespoonful into the simmering broth, making a total of 16 balls (the scallop mixture will be soft). Return the broth to a simmer and cook, covered, stirring gently once or twice, until the fish balls are firm and cooked though, about 10 minutes. Gently stir in the cilantro and orange zest. Serve at once.

PER SERVING (1⅓ cups soup with 4 fish balls): 344 Cal, 6 g Fat, 1 g Sat Fat, 0 g Trans Fat, 134 mg Chol, 1479 mg Sod, 32 g Carb, 2 g Fib, 35 g Prot, 121 mg Calc. ***POINTS*** value: ***7.***

FOOD NOTE If you prefer this dish a little spicier, use a 14½-ounce can of diced tomatoes with jalapeños.

Cold Cucumber Soup with Crabmeat and Rye Croutons

HANDS-ON PREP **20 MIN**
COOK **5 MIN**
SERVES **4**

- **1** English cucumber, peeled and chopped
- **1½** cups reduced-sodium chicken broth
- **1¼** cups plain fat-free yogurt
- **¼** teaspoon salt
- **¼** teaspoon freshly ground pepper
- **1** tablespoon canola oil
- **3** garlic cloves, thinly sliced
- **2** slices rye bread, cut into ½-inch cubes
- **6** ounces cooked fresh or thawed frozen lump crabmeat, picked over

1 Put the cucumber and broth in a blender and puree. Transfer the mixture to a glass bowl or plastic container; whisk in the yogurt, salt, and pepper until smooth. Cover the soup and refrigerate until chilled, at least 1 hour or up to 3 days.

2 Meanwhile, heat the oil in a large nonstick skillet over medium heat. Add the garlic and bread; cook, stirring frequently, until the bread is just toasted, about 6 minutes. Transfer the croutons to a plate and spread in a single layer; let cool. (The croutons can be stored in an airtight container up to 3 days.)

3 Serve the chilled soup sprinkled with the crab and croutons.

PER SERVING (1¼ cups soup with ¼ of crab and ⅓ cup croutons): 132 Cal, 1 g Fat, 0 g Sat Fat, 0 g Trans Fat, 47 mg Chol, 670 mg Sod, 15 g Carb, 2 g Fib, 16 g Prot, 149 mg Calc. ***POINTS*** value: ***2.***

HOW WE DID IT Whatever variety of crabmeat you select, be aware it can contain lots of flexible shell so it must be picked over carefully before using. To do this, use your fingers to lightly squeeze the lumps of meat, feeling for any hard or sharp pieces. Lumps of crabmeat are preferable to shreds, so work gently to keep the pieces intact as much as possible.

COLD CUCUMBER SOUP WITH CRABMEAT AND RYE CROUTONS

Shrimp Bisque

HANDS-ON PREP **15 MIN**
COOK **40 MIN**
SERVES **4**

- **¾ pound medium shrimp, peeled and deveined (reserve the shells)**
- **3 cups reduced-sodium chicken or vegetable broth, or 3 (8-ounce) bottles clam juice**
- **2½ cups water**
- **2 teaspoons unsalted butter**
- **2 shallots, chopped**
- **¼ cup long-grain white rice**
- **1 tablespoon tomato paste**
- **¼ teaspoon salt**
- **Pinch cayenne**
- **3 tablespoons dry sherry (optional)**

1 Combine the shrimp shells, broth, and water in a large saucepan; bring to a boil. Reduce the heat and simmer until the flavors are blended, about 10 minutes. Strain the broth mixture through a fine sieve into a bowl; discard the shells and set the broth aside.

2 Meanwhile, melt the butter in another large saucepan over medium heat. Add the shallots and cook, stirring occasionally, until softened, about 5 minutes. Stir in the reserved broth mixture, the rice, and tomato paste; bring to a boil. Reduce the heat and simmer until the rice is tender, about 20 minutes.

3 Stir in the shrimp, salt, and cayenne; cook until shrimp are just opaque in the center, about 3 minutes. With a slotted spoon, transfer 8 of the shrimp to a cutting board; chop and set aside. Let the soup cool about 5 minutes.

4 Pour the soup in batches into a blender and puree. Return the soup to the pan, stir in the sherry (if using) and simmer until heated through. Serve the soup sprinkled with the reserved shrimp.

PER SERVING (1 cup): 149 Cal, 3 g Fat, 1 g Sat Fat, 0 g Trans Fat, 131 mg Chol, 760 mg Sod, 13 g Carb, 0 g Fib, 17 g Prot, 33 mg Calc. ***POINTS*** value: ***3.***

GOOD IDEA Make this recipe an elegant do-ahead starter for a holiday celebration or any occasion when you want to treat yourself to something fancy. Just prepare the soup as directed through step 3; transfer the broth mixture and the reserved shrimp to separate airtight containers and refrigerate up to 2 days. Complete the recipe as directed, thinning the soup with a little broth or water if it becomes too thick.

Velvety Borscht

HANDS-ON PREP **10 MIN**
COOK **15 MIN**
SERVES **6**

2 teaspoons canola oil
1 onion, diced
1 stalk celery, thinly sliced
2 (14½-ounce) cans sliced beets, with liquid
3 cups reduced-sodium beef broth
1 teaspoon red-wine vinegar
Freshly ground pepper, to taste
6 tablespoons fat-free sour cream
Chopped fresh chives (optional)

1 Heat the oil in a large saucepan over medium heat. Add the onion and celery; cook, stirring occasionally, until very soft, about 10 minutes. Remove the pan from the heat; stir in the beets and broth. Pour the soup in batches into a blender and puree.
2 Return the soup to the pan, stir in the vinegar and pepper, and bring to a simmer. Garnish with sour cream and chives (if using).

PER SERVING (1¼ cups soup with 1 tablespoon sour cream): 79 Cal, 2 g Fat, 0 g Sat Fat, 0 g Trans Fat, 3 mg Chol, 516 mg Sod, 13 g Carb, 2 g Fib, 5 g Prot, 39 mg Calc. ***POINTS*** value: ***1.***

GOOD IDEA This soup is also delicious and refreshing served chilled, so it can be prepared in advance if you like. After blending, simply stir in the vinegar and pepper (there's no need to bring it to a simmer). Refrigerate until chilled, about 1 hour or transfer to an airtight container and refrigerate up to 3 days.

MINESTRONE WITH PARMESAN CRISPS

Minestrone with Parmesan Crisps

HANDS-ON PREP **25 MIN**
COOK **35 MIN**
SERVES **6**

- **7** cups vegetable broth
- **2** carrots, sliced
- **1** small zucchini, halved lengthwise and sliced ½-inch thick
- **1** onion, diced
- **1** celery stalk, sliced
- **3** garlic cloves, sliced
- **1** (15½-ounce) can pinto beans, rinsed and drained
- **1** (15½-ounce) can chickpeas, rinsed and drained
- **1** (14½-ounce) can diced tomatoes
- **1** cup ditalini or small elbow macaroni
- **1** tablespoon dried Italian seasoning
- **2** ounces Parmesan cheese, coarsely shredded (about ¾ cup)
- **⅓** cup chopped flat-leaf parsley

1 Combine the broth, carrots, zucchini, onion, celery, garlic, beans, chickpeas, tomatoes, pasta, and Italian seasoning in a large soup pot; bring to a boil. Reduce the heat and simmer until the vegetables are very tender, about 20 minutes.

2 Meanwhile, to make the Parmesan crisps, preheat the oven to 400°F. Line a baking sheet with foil; spray with nonstick spray. Sprinkle the cheese on the foil into a 9-inch square. Bake until very lightly browned, 8–10 minutes. Let cool completely on a rack. Break into 6 crisps.

3 Just before serving, stir the parsley into the soup. Serve with the Parmesan crisps.

PER SERVING (2 cups soup with 1 Parmesan crisp): 242 Cal, 4 g Fat, 2 g Sat Fat, 0 g Trans Fat, 8 mg Chol, 1,077 mg Sod, 39 g Carb, 8 g Fib, 12 g Prot, 239 mg Calc. ***POINTS*** value: ***4.***

HOW WE DID IT For best results, shred the Parmesan cheese for the crisps by using the large holes of a grater. If you own a silicone baking mat, sprinkle the cheese directly on it and bake as directed in step 2. The crisps can be made ahead and stored at room temperature in an airtight container up to 2 days.

Broccoli and Goat Cheese Soup

HANDS-ON PREP **15 MIN**
COOK **20 MIN**
SERVES **4**

- **1 tablespoon unsalted butter**
- **1 small onion, diced**
- **3 tablespoons all-purpose flour**
- **2 (14½-ounce) cans reduced-sodium chicken broth + enough water to equal 4 cups**
- **4 cups fresh broccoli florets**
- **1 ounce goat cheese, crumbled**
- **¼ teaspoon hot pepper sauce, or to taste**

1 Melt the butter in a large saucepan over medium heat. Add the onion and cook, stirring occasionally, until softened, about 5 minutes. Add the flour and cook, stirring constantly, until well blended and cooked through, about 1 minute. Gradually add the broth mixture, stirring constantly; bring to a boil. Reduce the heat and simmer, stirring occasionally, until the mixture thickens slightly, about 2 minutes. Add the broccoli and cook, stirring occasionally, until tender, 7–8 minutes. Let the mixture cool about 5 minutes.

2 Pour the soup in batches into a blender and puree. Return the soup to the pan; stir in the cheese and pepper sauce and cook over low heat until the cheese has melted. Serve at once.

PER SERVING (generous 1 cup): 109 Cal, 5 g Fat, 3 g Sat Fat, 0 g Trans Fat, 13 mg Chol, 607 mg sodium, 10 g Carb, 2 g Fib, 7 g Prot, 59 mg Calc. ***POINTS*** value: ***2***

Curried Parsnip Soup

HANDS-ON PREP **15 MIN**
COOK **30 MIN**
SERVES **6**

- **6 cups reduced-sodium chicken broth**
- **1 pound parsnips, peeled and thinly sliced**
- **½ onion, chopped**
- **1½ teaspoons curry powder**
- **2 tablespoons chopped fresh chives or scallions**

1 Combine the broth, parsnips, onion, and curry powder in a large saucepan; bring to a boil. Reduce the heat and simmer until the parsnips are very tender, about 25 minutes. Let the mixture cool about 5 minutes.

2 Pour the soup in batches into a blender and puree. Return the soup to the pan and simmer until heated through. Serve at once, sprinkled with the chives.

PER SERVING (1 cup soup with 1 teaspoon chives): 87 Cal, 0 g Fat, 0 g Sat Fat, 0 g Trans Fat, 0 mg Chol, 823 mg Sod, 18 g Carb, 4 g Fib, 4 g Prot, 36 mg Calc. ***POINTS*** value: ***1.***

FOOD NOTE Parsnips look like ivory-colored carrots, and you should choose them the same way you do their orange brethren: Don't buy huge, oversize specimens (they could be tough and woody), and take a pass if they're limp or shriveled.

Egg Drop Soup with Asparagus

HANDS-ON PREP **10 MIN**
COOK **15 MIN**
SERVES **4**

- **¾ pound fresh asparagus, trimmed and cut into ¾-inch pieces**
- **4 cups reduced-sodium chicken broth**
- **¼ cup cold water**
- **3 tablespoons cornstarch**
- **2 large eggs, lightly beaten**
- **2 teaspoons reduced-sodium soy sauce**
- **½ teaspoon rice-wine or white-wine vinegar**
- **Ground white pepper, to taste**

1 Bring a small saucepan of lightly salted water to a boil. Add the asparagus and cook until crisp-tender, about 3 minutes. Drain in a colander. Rinse the asparagus under cold running water; drain and set aside.
2 Meanwhile, bring the broth to a boil in a large saucepan. Whisk together the water and cornstarch in a cup until smooth and whisk into the broth. Simmer until the mixture thickens slightly, about 2 minutes.
3 Reduce the heat until the broth barely simmers. Slowly drizzle the eggs into the soup, while stirring quickly in a circular motion; cook about 1 minute. Gently stir in the soy sauce, vinegar, and white pepper. Divide the asparagus among 4 bowls and ladle the soup on top. Serve at once.

PER SERVING (1¼ cups): 87 Cal, 3 g Fat, 1 g Sat Fat, 0 g Trans Fat, 106 mg Chol, 758 mg Sod, 8 g Carb, 1 g Fib, 7 g Prot, 21 mg Calc. ***POINTS*** value: ***2.***

MAKE IT CORE We like the extra thickness a little cornstarch gives this Chinese restaurant-style soup, but if you're following the **Core Plan,** you can omit it—along with the ¼ cup cold water. Simply bring the broth to a boil and then proceed to step 3. The soup will be just as delicious.

EGG DROP SOUP WITH ASPARAGUS

Smoky and Creamy Corn Soup

HANDS-ON PREP **10 MIN**
COOK **25 MIN**
SERVES **4**

2 teaspoons olive oil
1 onion, chopped
1 red bell pepper, seeded and coarsely chopped
1 celery stalk, coarsely chopped
1 (16-ounce) bag frozen roasted corn kernels
4 cups vegetable broth
½ teaspoon chipotle chili powder

1 Heat the oil in a large nonstick saucepan over medium-high heat. Add the onion, bell pepper, and celery; cook, stirring frequently, until lightly browned, about 8 minutes.
2 Add the corn, 1 cup of the broth, and the chili powder; bring to a boil. Reduce the heat and simmer, covered, until the vegetables are softened, about 3 minutes. Let the mixture cool about 5 minutes. Pour the mixture in batches into a food processor or blender and puree.
3 Return the mixture to the pan. Add the remaining 3 cups broth and cook, stirring occasionally, until heated through, about 10 minutes.

PER SERVING (1½ cups): 178 Cal, 4 g Fat, 1 g Sat Fat, 0 g Trans Fat, 0 mg Chol, 1,023 mg Sod, 36 g Carb, 5 g Fib, 7 g Prot, 21 mg Calc. ***POINTS*** value: ***3.***

FOOD NOTE If you can't find frozen roasted corn kernels, use regular frozen corn kernels.

Thai Coconut-Vegetable Soup

HANDS-ON PREP **10 MIN**
COOK **20 MIN**
SERVES **6**

- **4 cups vegetable broth**
- **1 cup water**
- **¼ pound fresh shiitake mushrooms, stems discarded and caps thinly sliced**
- **2 carrots, thinly sliced**
- **1 Thai or serrano pepper, seeded and minced (wear gloves to prevent irritation)**
- **¾ cup light (reduced-fat) coconut milk**
- **2 plum tomatoes, chopped**
- **4 scallions, sliced**
- **¾ cup lightly packed fresh cilantro leaves**
- **4 teaspoons fresh lime juice**
- **2 teaspoons Asian fish sauce (nam pla)**

1 Combine the broth, water, mushrooms, carrots, and Thai pepper in a large saucepan; bring to a boil. Reduce the heat and simmer until the vegetables are tender, about 10 minutes.
2 Stir in the coconut milk, tomatoes, and scallions; bring just to a simmer. Remove the pan from heat. Stir in the cilantro, lime juice, and fish sauce and serve at once.

PER SERVING (1 cup): 53 Cal, 2 g Fat, 1 g Sat Fat, 0 g Trans Fat, 0 mg Chol, 533 mg Sod, 9 g Carb, 1 g Fib, 2 g Prot, 30 mg Calc. ***POINTS*** value: ***1.***

TRY IT Don't let the small size of Thai chiles fool you! This diminutive pepper packs a fiery punch that doesn't dissipate with cooking. Thai chiles range in color from green to red when fully ripe. They're available in Asian markets and some supermarkets.

ROASTED TOMATO AND WILD RICE SOUP

Roasted Tomato and Wild Rice Soup

HANDS-ON PREP **15 MIN**
COOK **1 HR 10 MIN**
SERVES **6**

- **5 teaspoons olive oil**
- **2 carrots, diced**
- **1 small fennel bulb, trimmed and diced**
- **1 onion, diced**
- **3 garlic cloves, sliced**
- **7½ cups water**
- **½ cup wild rice**
- **1 bay leaf**
- **1¼ teaspoons salt**
- **2 pints cherry tomatoes, halved**

1 Heat 2 teaspoons of the oil in a large saucepan over medium heat. Add the carrots, fennel, onion, and garlic; cook, stirring frequently, until lightly browned, about 7 minutes. Add the water, rice, bay leaf, and salt; bring to a boil. Reduce the heat and simmer until the grains start to pop and the rice is tender, about 45 minutes.

2 Meanwhile, preheat the oven to 475°F. Toss the tomatoes with the remaining 3 teaspoons oil and place cut-side down on a large rimmed baking sheet. Roast until the skins are shriveled and just begin to brown, about 20 minutes.

3 Add the roasted tomatoes and their juices to the rice mixture in the saucepan. Cook until heated through, about 5 minutes. Discard the bay leaf before serving.

PER SERVING (1¼ cups): 144 Cal, 4 g Fat, 1 g Sat Fat, 0 g Trans Fat, 0 mg Chol, 530 mg Sod, 24 g Carb, 4 g Fib, 4 g Prot, 41 mg Calc. ***POINTS*** value: ***2.***

HOW WE DID IT We prefer to use cherry tomatoes in this recipe because they generally have good flavor year-round and they roast quickly in a hot oven. But if plum tomatoes are in season, by all means use them. Just cut each tomato in half lengthwise and roast as directed except increase the cooking time by 5 to 10 minutes.

Miso Noodle Soup

HANDS-ON PREP **10 MIN**
COOK **20 MIN**
SERVES **6**

- **6 ounces udon noodles**
- **5 cups reduced-sodium vegetable broth**
- **¼ cup light miso**
- **½ medium head bok choy, sliced (about 2 cups)**
- **1 red bell pepper, seeded and cut into strips**
- **¼ pound fresh shiitake mushrooms, stems discarded and caps thinly sliced**
- **4 scallions, sliced**
- **½ teaspoon rice or white-wine vinegar**

1 Cook the noodles according to package directions; drain in a colander. Rinse the noodles under cold running water; drain and set aside.

2 Meanwhile, whisk together the broth and miso in a large saucepan. Add the bok choy, bell pepper, and mushrooms; bring to a boil. Reduce the heat and simmer, stirring occasionally, until the vegetables are just tender, about 7 minutes. Stir in reserved noodles, the scallions, and vinegar; serve at once.

PER SERVING (1 cup): 125 Cal, 1 g Fat, 0 g Sat Fat, 0 g Trans Fat, 0 mg Chol, 1,115 mg Sod, 24 g Carb, 1 g Fib, 4 g Prot, 50 mg Calc. ***POINTS*** value: ***2.***

TRY IT *Miso* (MEE-soh), a fermented soy paste, is found in the refrigerated section of Asian markets, natural-foods stores, and some supermarkets. If you have a choice between light and dark miso, go for the light variety—it's milder and less salty.

Warm Pear Soup with Ginger and Hazelnuts

HANDS-ON PREP **15 MIN**
COOK **15 MIN**
SERVES **4**

- **3 very ripe pears, such as Bosc or Bartlett, peeled and coarsely chopped**
- **2 cups unsweetened apple juice**
- **1 (1-inch) piece fresh ginger, peeled and thinly sliced**
- **1 cup pear juice**
- **2 tablespoons coarsely chopped toasted hazelnuts**

1 Combine the pears, apple juice, and ginger in a large saucepan; bring to a boil. Reduce the heat and simmer, covered, until the pears are very tender, 5–10 minutes (depending on the ripeness of the fruit). Let the mixture cool about 5 minutes.

2 Pour the mixture in batches into a blender and puree. Return the mixture to the pan and stir in the pear juice. Cook over low heat just until warm. Ladle the soup into bowls and sprinkle with the hazelnuts. Serve at once.

PER SERVING (1¼ cups soup with ½ tablespoon hazelnuts): 142 Cal, 2 g Fat, 0 g Sat Fat, 0 g Trans Fat, 0 mg Chol, 8 mg Sod, 31 g Carb, 2 g Fib, 1 g Prot, 25 mg Calc. ***POINTS*** value: ***3.***

GOOD IDEA This soup can be prepared ahead and served chilled. Transfer to an airtight container and refrigerate up to 2 days. Sprinkle with the hazelnuts just before serving.

CHAPTER FOUR

SANDWICHES

AND PIZZAS

STEAK AND CARAMELIZED ONION SANDWICH

Steak and Caramelized Onion Sandwich

HANDS-ON PREP **10 MIN**
COOK **20 MIN**
SERVES **4**

- **1** teaspoon olive oil
- **3** onions, thinly sliced
- **2** teaspoons sugar
- **¼** teaspoon dried thyme
- **2** teaspoons balsamic vinegar
- **¾** teaspoon salt
- **¼** teaspoon freshly ground pepper
- **1** (1-pound) flank steak, trimmed
- **2** tablespoons Dijon mustard
- **8** slices rye bread
- **1** medium tomato, cut into 8 thin slices

1 Heat the oil in a medium nonstick skillet over medium-high heat. Add the onions, sugar, and thyme; cook, stirring occasionally, until the onions are golden, about 10 minutes. Add the vinegar, ¼ teaspoon of the salt, and ⅛ teaspoon of the pepper; cook, stirring constantly, until the vinegar evaporates, about 30 seconds. Remove the skillet from the heat.

2 Meanwhile, spray the broiler rack with nonstick spray and preheat the broiler.

3 Sprinkle the steak with the remaining ½ teaspoon salt and ⅛ teaspoon pepper; place on the broiler rack. Broil the steak 5 inches from the heat until an instant-read thermometer inserted in the center of the steak registers 145°F for medium, about 4 minutes on each side. Transfer the steak to a cutting board and let stand about 5 minutes. Cut the steak on an angle against the grain into 12 slices.

4 Spread ¾ teaspoon of the mustard on each slice of bread. Divide the steak among 4 of the bread slices, then top each with 2 tomato slices, ¼ cup of the onions, and a slice of the remaining bread. Cut each sandwich in half and serve at once.

PER SERVING (1 sandwich): 398 Cal, 12 g Fat, 5 g Sat Fat, 0 g Trans Fat, 54 mg Chol, 1,120 mg Sod, 43 g Carb, 4 g Fib, 30 g Prot, 79 mg Calc. ***POINTS*** value: ***8.***

GOOD IDEA These hearty sandwiches are equally tasty served at room temperature or even chilled, so you might like to serve half a sandwich for lunch the next day (just wrap and keep refrigerated until ready to eat).

Grilled Ham and Cheese Panini

HANDS-ON PREP **10 MIN**
COOK **10 MIN**
SERVES **4**

- **4 teaspoons Dijon mustard**
- **1 tablespoon balsamic vinegar**
- **8 slices sourdough bread**
- **8 thin slices part-skim mozzarella cheese (about 2 ounces)**
- **½ pound thinly sliced ham**
- **1 tomato, cut into 8 slices**
- **12 fresh basil leaves**

1 Combine the mustard and vinegar in a small bowl; spread 1½ teaspoons on each of 4 slices of the bread. Layer each with 1 slice cheese, one-quarter of the ham, 1 slice tomato, 3 basil leaves, 1 slice tomato, 1 slice cheese, and 1 slice bread to make 4 sandwiches.

2 Spray a ridged grill pan with nonstick spray and set over medium-high heat or heat a panini sandwich maker according to manufacturers' instructions. Add the sandwiches (in batches if necessary). Cover with a heavy skillet filled with 1 or 2 cans. Grill until the bread is well marked and the cheese melts, 3–4 minutes on each side. (For the sandwich maker, grill 3–4 minutes.) Cut each sandwich in half and serve at once.

PER SERVING (1 sandwich): 285 Cal, 6 g Fat, 3 g Sat Fat, 0 g Trans Fat, 23 mg Chol, 1,240 mg Sod, 36 g Carb, 2 g Fib, 19 g Prot, 158 mg Calc. ***POINTS*** value: ***6.***

TRY IT These sandwiches would also be excellent if you used *ciabatta* (chyah-BAH-tah), a soft Italian bread with a thin, crisp crust, instead of the sourdough. Look for individual ciabatta rolls or a loaf that you can have the bakery slice.

GRILLED HAM AND CHEESE PANINI

Chicken Pita Pizzas

HANDS-ON PREP **10 MIN**
COOK **3 MIN**
SERVES **4**

1 Preheat the broiler. Place the pita breads on a baking sheet. Broil 4–5 inches from the heat until golden, about 45 seconds on each side.
2 Spread 3 tablespoons of the hummus evenly onto each of the pita breads, almost to the edge. Top each evenly with the chicken, and sprinkle with the cheese, then the olives. Broil the pizzas until the cheese melts, 50–70 seconds.

PER SERVING (1 pizza): 220 Cal, 8 g Fat, 1 g Sat Fat, 0 g Trans fat, 30 mg Chol, 509 mg Sod, 21 g Carb, 2 g Fib, 17 g Prot, 142 mg Calc. ***POINTS*** value: ***5.***

TRY IT *Hummus* (HOOM-uhs), a high-fiber Middle Eastern chickpea dip, is available in countless flavors, such as black olive, sun-dried tomato, cracked pepper, or chili. Try experimenting with some as an alternative to the scallion variety we've called for here and serve leftover hummus with raw veggies for a healthy snack.

- **2 (7-inch) pocketless pita breads**
- **6 tablespoons scallion hummus**
- **1 (½-pound) bone-in roasted chicken breast, skin and bone removed and chicken coarsely shredded**
- **½ cup shredded part-skim mozzarella cheese**
- **6 pitted large manzanilla or Sicilian green olives, chopped**

Turkey-Mango Wraps with Chipotle Mayonnaise

HANDS-ON PREP **15 MIN**
COOK **NONE**
SERVES **4**

- **6** **tablespoons fat-free mayonnaise**
- **1½** **teaspoons minced chipotle en adobo**
- **1** **teaspoon grated lime zest**
- **4** **(8-inch) fat-free flour tortillas**
- **4** **Boston lettuce leaves**
- **1** **mango, peeled, pitted, and cut into 16 slices**
- **¾** **pound thinly sliced roasted turkey breast**
- **½** **Hass avocado, pitted, peeled, and cut into 8 slices**

1 Combine the mayonnaise, chipotle en adobo, and lime zest in a small bowl.

2 Spread one-quarter of the chipotle mayonnaise on each tortilla. Layer each with 1 lettuce leaf, 4 mango slices, one-quarter of the turkey, and 2 avocado slices. Fold the sides over and roll up to enclose the filling. Cut the rolls in half on a slight diagonal.

PER SERVING (1 wrap): 257 Cal, 6 g Fat, 2 g Sat Fat, 0 g Trans Fat, 37 mg Chol, 1,561 mg Sod, 35 g Carb, 7 g Fib, 19 g Prot, 95 mg Calc. ***POINTS*** value: ***5.***

TRY IT *Chipotles en adobo* (chih-POHT-lay en ah-DOH-boh) are smoked jalapeño peppers canned in a tangy adobo sauce of tomato, vinegar, and spices. Look for them in Hispanic markets or the ethnic foods section of most supermarkets. If you can't find chipotles en adobo, substitute an equal amount tomato sauce with a generous pinch of cayenne.

Halibut Sandwiches with Tartar Sauce

HANDS-ON PREP **10 MIN**
COOK **5 MIN**
SERVES **4**

- **¼ cup low-fat mayonnaise**
- **2 tablespoons sweet pickle relish**
- **1 tablespoon drained capers**
- **4 whole-wheat hamburger buns**
- **2 ounces reduced-fat sharp cheddar cheese, cut into 12 thin slices**
- **4 (¼-pound) skinless halibut fillets**
- **¾ teaspoon salt**
- **⅛ teaspoon freshly ground pepper**
- **4 small lettuce leaves**
- **4 thin red onion slices**
- **1 medium tomato, cut into 4 (¼-inch-thick) slices**

1 Preheat the broiler. To make the tartar sauce, combine the mayonnaise, relish, and capers in a small bowl and set aside.
2 Arrange the hamburger buns, cut-side up, on a large baking sheet. Divide the cheese among the top halves of the buns.
3 Sprinkle the halibut with the salt and pepper. Spray a ridged grill pan with nonstick spray and set over medium-high heat. Add the fillets and cook until well marked and just opaque in the center, 2–3 minutes on each side.
4 Meanwhile, broil the buns 5 inches from the heat until lightly toasted and the cheese melts, about 1 minute. Layer 1 lettuce leaf, 1 fillet, 1 slice red onion, 1 slice tomato, and about 1½ tablespoons of the tartar sauce on each of the bottom halves of the buns. Cover with the top halves of the buns and serve at once.

PER SERVING (1 sandwich): 310 Cal, 8 g Fat, 2 g Sat Fat, 0 g Trans Fat, 43 mg Chol, 1,057 mg Sod, 32 g Carb, 4 g Fib, 32 g Prot, 193 mg Calc. ***POINTS*** value: ***6.***

GOOD IDEA If you can't find halibut at your local fish store or supermarket, these sandwiches are also terrific with cod or haddock (the cooking time will remain the same).

Tarragon Shrimp Salad Wraps

HANDS-ON PREP **10 MIN**
COOK **5 MIN**
SERVES **4**

- **1 pound peeled and deveined medium shrimp**
- **½ teaspoon salt**
- **¼ teaspoon freshly ground pepper**
- **1 teaspoon extra-virgin olive oil**
- **½ small red onion, chopped**
- **½ small red bell pepper, seeded and chopped**
- **1 celery stalk, chopped**
- **¼ cup reduced-fat mayonnaise**
- **1 tablespoon chopped fresh tarragon, or 1 teaspoon dried**
- **2 teaspoons fresh lemon juice**
- **4 Boston lettuce leaves**
- **4 (8-inch) fat-free flour tortillas**

1 Sprinkle the shrimp with the salt and pepper. Heat the oil in a large nonstick skillet over medium-high heat. Add the shrimp and cook, stirring occasionally, just until opaque in the center, about 4 minutes. Transfer the shrimp to a bowl and let cool 5 minutes. Add the red onion, bell pepper, celery, mayonnaise, tarragon, and lemon juice; mix well.

2 Arrange 1 lettuce leaf and one-quarter of the shrimp mixture on each tortilla. Fold the sides over and roll up to enclose the filling. Cut the rolls in half on a slight diagonal and serve at once.

PER SERVING (1 wrap): 242 Cal, 7 g Fat, 1 g Sat Fat, 0 g Trans Fat, 173 mg Chol, 958 mg Sod, 22 g Carb, 4 g Fib, 23 g Prot, 120 mg Calc. ***POINTS*** value: ***5.***

MAKE IT CORE To make this wrap **Core Plan**-friendly, use fat-free mayonnaise and skip the tortillas, wrapping the shrimp salad in 2 lettuce leaves instead (you'll also reduce the per-serving ***POINTS*** value to 3).

Curried Egg Salad Sandwiches

HANDS-ON PREP **10 MIN**
COOK **NONE**
SERVES **4**

- **¼ cup golden raisins**
- **7 large hard-cooked eggs, halved**
- **¼ cup reduced-fat mayonnaise**
- **1 scallion, chopped**
- **2 tablespoons chopped fresh cilantro**
- **2 tablespoons sweet pickle relish**
- **1½ teaspoons Dijon mustard**
- **1 teaspoon Madras curry powder**
- **¼ teaspoon salt**
- **⅛ teaspoon freshly ground pepper**
- **8 slices whole-wheat bread**

1 Combine the raisins with enough warm water to cover by 2 inches in a small bowl. Let stand until the raisins soften, about 10 minutes. Drain.

2 Meanwhile, discard 3 of the egg yolks. Chop the whites with the remaining eggs and transfer to a large bowl. Stir in the mayonnaise, scallion, cilantro, relish, mustard, curry powder, salt, pepper, and the softened raisins.

3 Spread ½ cup egg salad on each of 4 bread slices. Top with the remaining 4 bread slices.

PER SERVING (1 sandwich): 319 Cal, 13 g Fat, 3 g Sat Fat, 0 g Trans Fat, 218 mg Chol, 761 mg Sod, 39 g Carb, 5 g Fib, 15 g Prot, 80 mg Calc. ***POINTS*** value: ***7.***

GOOD IDEA Wrap one of these sandwiches to tote to the office for a nutritious and satisfying lunch. Be sure to keep the sandwich refrigerated or in an insulated carrying pack at the office. If you have extra egg salad, it will keep, refrigerated, in an airtight container up to 2 days.

Greek Salad Pitas

HANDS-ON PREP **15 MIN**
COOK **5 MIN**
SERVES **4**

- **1** large cucumber, peeled, halved lengthwise, and seeded
- **1** (8-ounce) container plain fat-free yogurt
- **½** small garlic clove, minced
- **½** teaspoon salt
- **2** cups shredded romaine lettuce
- **1** large tomato, chopped
- **½** green bell pepper, seeded and chopped
- **1** small onion, thinly sliced
- **¾** cup crumbled reduced-fat feta cheese
- **1** tablespoon red-wine vinegar
- **2** teaspoons extra-virgin olive oil
- **4** (6-inch) whole-wheat pita breads with pockets

1 Preheat the oven to 350°F.

2 Cut the cucumber crosswise into 4 equal pieces. Shred 1 piece of the cucumber on a box grater; squeeze out the excess liquid and transfer the shredded cucumber to a small bowl. Stir in the yogurt, garlic, and salt.

3 Chop the remaining cucumber and transfer to a large bowl. Add the lettuce, tomato, bell pepper, onion, cheese, vinegar, and oil; mix well.

4 Cut the top third off each pita bread and discard. Place the pita pockets on a baking sheet and bake until heated through, about 5 minutes.

5 Place ¾ cup of the salad mixture in each of 4 pita pockets. Drizzle each with 1½ tablespoons of the yogurt mixture, then add ¾ cup more salad mixture. Drizzle the tops evenly with the remaining yogurt mixture. Serve at once.

PER SERVING (1 sandwich): 287 Cal, 7 g Fat, 2 g Sat Fat, 0 g Trans Fat, 9 mg Chol, 951 mg Sod, 48 g Carb, 7 g Fib, 15 g Prot, 149 mg Calc. ***POINTS*** value: ***6.***

GOOD IDEA While you are prepping the bell pepper for this recipe, cut the remaining half into sticks and you'll have a light and crunchy bite at the ready when your next snack attack strikes.

GOLDEN ONION PIZZA SQUARES WITH TOMATO AND GOAT CHEESE

Golden Onion Pizza Squares with Tomato and Goat Cheese

HANDS-ON PREP **25 MIN**
COOK **40 MIN**
SERVES **6**

- **1** teaspoon olive oil
- **1** Vidalia onion or 2 yellow onions, halved and thinly sliced
- **¼** teaspoon salt
- **2** teaspoons butter
- **8** plum tomatoes, chopped (about 3½ cups)
- **1** teaspoon sugar
- **1** tablespoon balsamic vinegar
- **1** pound prepared fresh or thawed frozen pizza or bread dough
- **4** ounces goat cheese, crumbled
- **10** niçoise or other small oil-cured black olives, pitted and chopped
- **1** tablespoon chopped fresh thyme, or 1 teaspoon dried

1 Heat the oil in a large nonstick skillet over medium heat. Add the onion and salt; cook, stirring frequently, until the onion is golden, about 15 minutes. Transfer the onion to a plate and set aside.
2 Melt the butter in the same skillet. Add the tomatoes and sugar; cook, stirring frequently, until most of the liquid has evaporated, about 10 minutes. Add the vinegar and simmer about 1 minute.
3 Meanwhile, arrange one rack on the bottom rung of the oven. Preheat the oven to 450°F.
4 With floured hands, stretch and press the pizza dough onto the bottom of a 10½ x 15½-inch nonstick jelly-roll pan. Spread the onion mixture onto the dough. Spoon the tomato mixture on top. Sprinkle with the cheese, olives, and thyme.
5 Bake on the bottom rack of the oven until the crust is golden and the cheese is slightly melted, 15–20 minutes. Cut into 6 squares and serve at once.

PER SERVING (1 square): 310 Cal, 10 g Fat, 5 g Sat Fat, 0 g Trans fat, 18 mg Chol, 623 mg Sod, 45 g Carb, 3 g Fib, 10 g Prot, 128 mg Calc. ***POINTS*** value: ***6.***

EXPRESS LANE To get a jumpstart on the prep, in addition to having the pizza dough at the ready, sauté the onions as directed in step 1, then transfer to an airtight container and refrigerate overnight. Proceed with the recipe the next day as directed.

Mini Salad Pizzas

HANDS-ON PREP **20 MIN**
COOK **10 MIN**
SERVES **6**

- **1** pound prepared fresh or thawed frozen pizza or bread dough
- **4** ounces Gruyère cheese, shredded
- **2** tablespoons white balsamic vinegar
- **1** tablespoon olive oil
- **1** teaspoon honey
- **½** garlic clove, minced
- **½** teaspoon Dijon mustard
- **½** teaspoon ground coriander
- **½** teaspoon salt
- **Freshly ground pepper, to taste**
- **8** cups mesclun salad greens
- **1** small apple, diced
- **2** tablespoons chopped toasted walnuts

1 Adjust the racks to divide the oven into thirds. Preheat the oven to 450°F.
2 Divide the dough into 6 pieces. Sprinkle a work surface lightly with flour. Turn the dough onto the surface; knead lightly. With a lightly floured rolling pin, roll each piece of dough into a 6-inch circle. Transfer the dough circles to 2 large nonstick baking sheets; sprinkle with the cheese. Bake until the crusts are golden and the cheese melts, about 10 minutes, switching the pans between the racks halfway through the baking time. Transfer the crusts to a rack to cool slightly, 2–3 minutes.
3 Meanwhile, combine the vinegar, oil, honey, garlic, mustard, coriander, salt, and pepper in a bowl. Place the mesclun greens and apple in a large bowl; add the dressing and toss to coat. Spoon the salad over the warm crusts, then sprinkle with the walnuts. Serve at once.

PER SERVING (1 pizza): 315 Cal, 11 g Fat, 4 g Sat Fat, 0 g Trans fat, 21 mg Chol, 645 mg Sod, 43 g Carb, 4 g Fib, 12 g Prot, 294 mg Calc. ***POINTS*** value: ***6.***

TRY IT *Gruyère* (groo-YEHR) is a rich and nutty tasting cheese from Switzerland that melts beautifully. Or you can use domestic or imported Swiss cheese.

Two-Cheese Spinach Pizza

HANDS-ON PREP **5 MIN**
COOK **3 MIN**
SERVES **6**

- **1 (8-ounce) microwavable bag baby spinach leaves**
- **½ cup marinated artichoke hearts, rinsed, drained, and chopped**
- **1 (10-ounce) thin prebaked pizza crust**
- **½ cup shredded part-skim mozzarella cheese**
- **½ cup crumbled feta cheese**

1 Preheat the broiler. Microwave the spinach according to the package directions. Coarsely chop the spinach, place in a medium bowl, and stir in the artichokes.
2 Place the pizza crust on a pizza pan or baking sheet. Broil 4-5 inches from the heat until golden, 30-60 seconds on each side.
3 Spread the spinach mixture over the crust to within 1 inch of the edge. Sprinkle the mozzarella and feta cheeses evenly over the spinach. Broil until the mozzarella melts and the feta partially melts, 50-70 seconds. Cut into 6 wedges and serve at once.

PER SERVING (1 wedge): 221 Cal, 8 g Fat, 3 g Sat Fat, 0 g Trans fat, 17 mg Chol, 532 mg Sod, 27 g Carb, 3 g Fib, 10 g Prot, 288 mg Calc. ***POINTS*** value: ***4.***

GOOD IDEA If you don't have a microwave to cook the spinach, just place it in a large nonstick skillet with 1 tablespoon water. Cook the spinach over medium-high heat, stirring constantly, just until wilted, about 2 minutes.

Zesty Caponata Pizzas

HANDS-ON PREP **10 MIN**
COOK **3 MIN**
SERVES **4**

- **1 (8-ounce) package individual prebaked pizza crusts (two 6-inch crusts), split horizontally to make 4 rounds**
- **1 cup canned small white beans, rinsed and drained**
- **6 tablespoons prepared caponata, chopped**
- **2 tablespoons sliced hot cherry peppers in vinegar, chopped**
- **1 tablespoon vinegar from cherry peppers**
- **1 cup shredded light Italian 4-cheese blend (mozzarella, provolone, Asiago, and Romano)**

1 Preheat the broiler. Place the pizza crusts, split-sides up, on a baking sheet. Broil 4–5 inches from the heat until golden, 30-60 seconds on each side.

2 Meanwhile, combine the beans, caponata, cherry peppers, and vinegar in a bowl.

3 Top each of the crusts with a generous 1/4 cup of the bean mixture, spreading almost to the edge. Sprinkle each with 1/4 cup of the cheese. Broil until the cheese melts, about 1 minute and serve at once.

PER SERVING (1 pizza): 304 Cal, 10 g Fat, 3 g Sat Fat, 0 g Trans fat, 15 mg Chol, 852 mg Sod, 39 g Carb, 5 g Fib, 17 g Prot, 400 mg Calc. ***POINTS*** value: ***6.***

TRY IT *Caponata* (kap-oh-NAH-tah), a classic Sicilian compote made with sautéed eggplant, onion, garlic, tomato, herbs, and sometimes green olives, is readily available in cans or jars at the supermarket. Use any leftover caponata for making bruschetta: Simply top a toasted baguette slice with 1 tablespoon of the caponata.

ZESTY CAPONATA PIZZAS

CHAPTER FIVE

CHICKEN

PLUS!

CHICKEN ROASTED OVER SQUASH

Chicken Roasted Over Squash

HANDS-ON PREP **15 MIN**
COOK **1 HR 10 MIN**
SERVES **8**

- **1 onion, chopped**
- **1 red bell pepper, seeded and chopped**
- **1 medium kabocha squash, peeled, seeded, and cut into ½-inch pieces**
- **2 teaspoons chopped fresh thyme**
- **½ teaspoon salt**
- **Freshly ground pepper, to taste**
- **1 (4-pound) chicken, split in half and skinned**
- **2 tablespoons Dijon mustard**
- **1 tablespoon unsweetened applesauce**

1 Preheat the oven to 350°F.
2 Spray a large nonstick skillet with canola nonstick spray and set over medium heat. Add the onion and bell pepper; cook, stirring frequently, until slightly softened, about 3 minutes. Add the squash; cook, stirring frequently, about 4 minutes. Stir in the thyme, salt, and ground pepper, then mound the mixture in the center of a 9 x 13-inch baking pan.
3 Place the two halves of the chicken, like a tent, over the vegetables in the pan, making sure that all the vegetables are covered.
4 Stir together the mustard and applesauce in a small bowl until smooth; brush over the chicken. Bake the chicken until golden and an instant-read thermometer inserted in a thigh registers 180°F, about 1 hour. Transfer the chicken to a cutting board and let stand about 10 minutes before carving. Serve with the vegetables.

PER SERVING (⅛ of chicken with scant ½ cup vegetables): 224 Cal, 7 g Fat, 2 g Sat Fat, 0 g Trans Fat, 78 mg Chol, 320 mg Sod, 14 g Carb, 2 g Fib, 27 g Prot, 51 mg Calc. ***POINTS*** value: ***5.***

TRY IT Winter squash, such as *kabocha* (kah-BOH-chah) with sweet, smooth-textured orange flesh, are rich in nutrients and fiber, and very low in calories. If you can't find one, substitute other winter squash such as acorn squash (you'll need two for this recipe).

Chicken Smothered with Onion, Peppers, and Fennel Seeds

HANDS-ON PREP **15 MIN**
COOK **45 MIN**
SERVES **4**

2 teaspoons fennel seeds

2 (3/4-pound) bone-in chicken breast halves, skinned and cut crosswise in half

1 teaspoon salt

1/8 teaspoon cayenne

1 tablespoon olive oil

1 Spanish onion (about 1 pound), halved and thinly sliced

2 garlic cloves, minced

1 large red bell pepper, seeded and sliced

1 large green bell pepper, seeded and sliced

1/4 cup water

1 Sprinkle the fennel seeds in the bottom of a nonstick Dutch oven and cook over medium heat, shaking the pan occasionally, until toasted, about 5 minutes. Transfer to a plate to cool, then grind the fennel seeds in a spice grinder; set aside.

2 Sprinkle the chicken with the salt and cayenne. Heat the oil in the same Dutch oven over medium heat. Add the chicken and cook until lightly browned, about 3 minutes on each side; transfer to a plate and set aside.

3 Add the onion and garlic to the Dutch oven. Cook over medium heat, stirring frequently, until golden, about 10 minutes. Add the bell peppers, the chicken, and water; bring to a boil. Reduce the heat and simmer, covered, until the chicken is cooked through and the bell peppers are tender, about 20 minutes. Stir in the ground toasted fennel seeds.

PER SERVING (1 chicken breast half with about 1/3 cup bell peppers and sauce): 254 Cal, 8 g Fat, 2 g Sat Fat, 0 g Trans Fat, 74 mg Chol, 662 mg Sod, 17 g Carb, 4 g Fib, 29 g Prot, 56 mg Calc. ***POINTS*** value: ***5.***

FOOD NOTE If you don't have a spice grinder, you can crush the fennel seeds in a mortar and pestle. Or place between sheets of wax paper and crush with a meat mallet.

Oven-Fried Chicken Breasts

HANDS-ON PREP **15 MIN**
COOK **35 MIN**
SERVES **6**

- **1 cup fat-free milk**
- **6 tablespoons plain dried bread crumbs, preferably whole-wheat**
- **2 tablespoons ground pecans**
- **1 teaspoon paprika**
- **1 teaspoon celery seeds, crushed**
- **½ teaspoon ground cumin**
- **½ teaspoon onion powder**
- **½ teaspoon salt**
- **¼ teaspoon ground nutmeg**
- **Freshly ground pepper, to taste**
- **3 (¾-pound) bone-in chicken breast halves, skinned and cut crosswise in half**

1 Adjust the racks to divide the oven into thirds. Preheat the oven to 400°F. Line a rimmed baking sheet with parchment paper or a silicone baking mat.
2 Pour the milk into a medium bowl. Combine the bread crumbs, pecans, paprika, celery seeds, cumin, onion powder, salt, nutmeg, and pepper on a piece of wax paper.
3 Dip the chicken pieces in the milk, then coat them on all sides with the bread crumb mixture, pressing to make sure the spices adhere to the chicken. Discard the excess bread crumb mixture.
4 Spray each piece of chicken lightly with nonstick spray, then place, bone-side down, on the baking sheet. Bake in the lower third of the oven until browned and an instant-read thermometer inserted in a breast registers 170°F, about 35 minutes. Let the chicken stand about 5 minutes before serving.

PER SERVING (1 chicken breast half): 206 Cal, 7 g Fat, 1 g Sat Fat, 0 g Trans Fat, 74 mg Chol, 331 mg Sod, 7 g Carb, 1 g Fib, 29 g Prot, 59 mg Calc. ***POINTS*** value: ***5.***

HOW WE DID IT To prep the pecans for this recipe, grind them in a clean coffee or spice grinder until they are powdery, but not until they turn to a paste.

Hunter-Style Chicken

HANDS-ON PREP **5 MIN**
COOK **35 MIN**
SERVES **8**

- **1 (2½–3-pound) chicken, cut into 8 pieces and skinned**
- **½ teaspoon salt**
- **¼ teaspoon freshly ground pepper**
- **3 teaspoons olive oil**
- **1 onion, chopped**
- **3 garlic cloves, minced**
- **2 assorted color bell peppers, seeded and cut into ½-inch pieces**
- **¼ pound fresh white mushrooms, sliced**
- **1 celery stalk, chopped**
- **1 (1-pint) container refrigerated fresh tomato pasta sauce**
- **Fresh thyme sprigs (optional)**

1 Sprinkle the chicken with the salt and ground pepper. Heat 2 teaspoons of the oil in a large nonstick skillet over medium-high heat. Add the chicken and cook until browned, 3–4 minutes on each side. Transfer the chicken to a plate and set aside.

2 Heat the remaining 1 teaspoon oil in the same skillet over medium-high heat. Add the onion and garlic; cook, stirring occasionally, until softened, about 3 minutes. Add the bell peppers, mushrooms, and celery; cook, stirring occasionally, until softened, 5–6 minutes. Return the chicken to the skillet; add the pasta sauce and stir to coat. Bring the mixture to a boil. Reduce the heat and simmer, covered, until the chicken is cooked through and the vegetables are tender, about 20 minutes. Garnish with thyme sprigs (if using) and serve at once.

PER SERVING (1 piece chicken with scant ½ cup vegetables and sauce): 203 Cal, 8 g Fat, 2 g Sat Fat, 0 g Trans Fat, 49 mg Chol, 510 mg Sod, 16 g Carb, 2 g Fib, 18 g Prot, 33 mg Calc. ***POINTS*** value: ***4.***

FOOD NOTE "Hunter-style" refers to a dish cooked with onions, peppers, mushrooms, and tomatoes. You might be more familiar with its Italian name—*cacciatore* (kah-chuh-TOR-ee), which means hunter.

HUNTER-STYLE CHICKEN

Chicken Cooked with Grapes

HANDS-ON PREP **10 MIN**
COOK **25 MIN**
SERVES **4**

- **2 (3⁄4-pound) bone-in chicken breast halves, skinned and cut crosswise in half**
- **1⁄4 teaspoon salt**
- **Pinch freshly ground pepper**
- **1 tablespoon canola oil**
- **1 cup reduced-sodium chicken broth**
- **1⁄2 pound red seedless grapes on the stem, cut into 4 clusters**
- **1⁄4 cup chopped flat-leaf parsley**

1 Sprinkle the chicken with the salt and pepper. Heat the oil in a large nonstick skillet over medium heat. Add the chicken and cook until browned, 5–6 minutes on each side. Add the broth and bring to a boil. Reduce the heat and simmer, covered, until the chicken is cooked through, about 10 minutes. Add the grapes and simmer, covered, until the grapes are softened, about 2 minutes.
2 Using a slotted spatula, transfer the chicken to a plate. Add the grapes and sprinkle with the parsley.

PER SERVING (1 chicken breast half with 1 cluster grapes): 208 Cal, 7 g Fat, 1 g Sat Fat, 0 g Trans Fat, 68 mg Chol, 363 mg Sod, 11 g Carb, 1 g Fib, 26 g Prot, 24 mg Calc. ***POINTS*** value: ***5.***

GOOD IDEA Buy an extra bunch of grapes and freeze for a cool and nutritious snack.

Chicken with Mushrooms and Vermouth

HANDS-ON PREP **15 MIN**
COOK **1 HR**
SERVES **6**

- **3** (¾-pound) bone-in chicken breast halves, skinned and cut crosswise in half
- **1** large shallot, finely chopped
- **½** pound fresh white mushrooms, thinly sliced
- **½** cup dry vermouth
- **¾** cup reduced-sodium chicken broth
- **1** bay leaf
- **1** teaspoon chopped fresh thyme
- **¼** teaspoon salt
- **Freshly ground pepper, to taste**
- **1** tablespoon all-purpose flour
- **3** tablespoons water

1 Preheat the oven to 350°F.

2 Spray a Dutch oven or large flameproof casserole dish with nonstick spray and set over medium-high heat. Add the chicken and cook until browned, about 2 minutes on each side. Transfer to a plate and set aside.

3 Add the shallot to the same Dutch oven and cook, stirring frequently, until slightly softened, about 20 seconds. Add the mushrooms and cook 20 seconds, then stir in the vermouth, scraping up any browned bits from the bottom of the pot. Cook, stirring occasionally, until the mushrooms are softened and the liquid reduces by half, about 3 minutes.

4 Stir in the broth, bay leaf, thyme, salt, and pepper; bring to a boil. Meanwhile, combine the flour and water in a small bowl; mix to a smooth paste. Stir some of the hot broth mixture into the flour mixture, then add to the pot. Cook, stirring constantly, until the mixture bubbles and thickens, about 1 minute. Return the chicken and any accumulated juices to the pot.

5 Transfer the pot to the oven, cover and bake until the chicken is cooked through, 50 minutes. Discard the bay leaf before serving.

PER SERVING (1 chicken breast half with ⅓ cup mushroom sauce): 185 Cal, 4 g Fat, 1 g Sat Fat, 0 g Trans Fat, 74 mg Chol, 229 mg Sod, 5 g Carb, 1 g Fib, 29 g Prot, 23 mg Calc. ***POINTS*** value: ***4.***

GOOD IDEA We call for vermouth, instead of white wine, for two reasons: Vermouth is an herbed variation of white wine, a better foil to casseroles and the like. But vermouth is also a fortified wine, so it will stay fresh for months if the bottle is kept sealed in a cool, dark place. White wine can turn acidic quickly, within a few days of opening—so it can never be a pantry staple.

Baked Chicken Breast Packets

HANDS-ON PREP **20 MIN**
COOK **35 MIN**
SERVES **4**

- **4 (¼-pound) skinless boneless chicken breast halves**
- **2 cups cubed yellow squash**
- **12 cherry tomatoes, halved**
- **12 pitted green olives, rinsed and chopped**
- **8 fresh basil leaves**
- **4 teaspoons dry vermouth**

1 Preheat the oven to 450°F. Cut 4 (12-inch) sheets of foil or parchment paper.
2 Place 1 chicken breast half on each sheet of foil; top each with ½ cup of the squash, 6 tomato halves, 1 tablespoon chopped olives, and 2 basil leaves. Sprinkle 1 teaspoon vermouth over each. Crimp the foil into packets, making a tight seal.
3 Place the packets on a rimmed baking sheet and bake until the chicken is cooked through and the squash is tender, about 35 minutes. Let the packets stand about 5 minutes, then open them with care to avoid getting a steam burn. Serve, drizzled with any juices.

PER SERVING (1 chicken breast half with ⅔ cup vegetables and sauce): 188 Cal, 5 g Fat, 1 g Sat Fat, 0 g Trans Fat, 68 mg Chol, 312 mg Sod, 8 g Carb, 2 g Fib, 26 g Prot, 31 mg Calc. ***POINTS*** value: ***4.***

MAKE IT CORE If you follow the **Core Plan,** instead of using vermouth, simply sprinkle the chicken with fresh lemon juice or reduced-sodium chicken broth in step 2.

Chicken, Cheddar, and Apple Wraps

HANDS-ON PREP **15 MIN**
COOK **NONE**
SERVES **4**

5 teaspoons Dijon mustard

1 tablespoon honey

4 iceberg lettuce leaves

2 ounces reduced-fat sharp cheddar cheese, cut into 12 strips

½ pound thinly sliced cooked chicken breast

1 Granny Smith apple, peeled and cut into 16 slices

4 (8-inch) fat-free flour tortillas

¼ teaspoon salt

⅛ teaspoon freshly ground pepper

1 Combine the mustard and honey in a small bowl.
2 Layer 1 lettuce leaf, 3 cheese strips, one-quarter of the chicken, and 4 apple slices onto each tortilla; sprinkle with the salt and pepper. Drizzle each with 2 teaspoons of the mustard mixture; fold the sides over and roll up to enclose the filling. Cut the rolls in half on a slight diagonal.

PER SERVING (1 wrap): 270 Cal, 6 g Fat, 3 g Sat Fat, 0 g Trans Fat, 58 mg Chol, 820 mg Sod, 28 g Carb, 4 g Fib, 26 g Prot, 189 mg Calc. ***POINTS*** value: ***5.***

TRY IT Substitute sun-dried tomato, spinach, or whole-wheat flour tortillas in this recipe if desired.

CHICKEN WITH RICE NOODLES, SCALLIONS, AND CARROTS

Chicken with Rice Noodles, Scallions, and Carrots

HANDS-ON PREP **15 MIN**
COOK **15 MIN**
SERVES **4**

4 ounces rice noodles

2 cups reduced-sodium chicken broth

2 tablespoons reduced-sodium soy sauce

2 tablespoons honey

4 quarter-size slices peeled fresh ginger

3 star anise pods

1 pound skinless boneless chicken breasts, cut into 1½-inch chunks

4 scallions, cut into 1-inch pieces

2 carrots, thinly sliced

2 tablespoons thinly sliced fresh mint (optional)

1 Cook the rice noodles according to package directions; drain and divide among 4 large shallow bowls.
2 Meanwhile, combine the broth, soy sauce, honey, ginger, and star anise in a large skillet; bring to a boil. Reduce the heat and simmer until the flavors are blended, about 5 minutes. Add the chicken, scallions, and carrots; return to a simmer. Cook, covered, until the chicken is cooked through and the carrots are tender, 10–12 minutes. Discard the ginger and star anise.
3 Top each bowl of noodles with one-quarter of the chicken and the broth mixture. Sprinkle evenly with the mint (if using).

PER SERVING (1 bowl): 339 Cal, 5 g Fat, 1 g Sat Fat, 0 g Trans Fat, 68 mg Chol, 927 mg Sod, 39 g Carb, 2 g Fib, 32 g Prot, 50 mg Calc. ***POINTS*** value: ***7.***

TRY IT Star anise is a star-shaped pod with a distinctive licorice-anise flavor. It originated in China and is a key component of Chinese five-spice powder. If you can't find star anise at your local supermarket or Asian grocery store, you can substitute ¼ teaspoon anise seeds tied in a small cheesecloth bag for every star anise pod.

Chicken Kebabs with Corn and Zucchini Salad

HANDS-ON PREP **20 MIN**
COOK **10 MIN**
SERVES **4**

- **3 tablespoons fresh lime juice**
- **2 tablespoons white-wine vinegar**
- **2 teaspoons olive oil**
- **2 garlic cloves, minced**
- **½ teaspoon salt**
- **1 pound skinless boneless chicken breasts, cut into 1½-inch chunks**
- **1–2 teaspoons chipotle chili powder**
- **2 cups fresh or thawed frozen corn kernels**
- **1 zucchini, finely diced (about 1½ cups)**
- **1 small onion, chopped**
- **3 tablespoons chopped fresh cilantro**
- **Pinch cayenne**

1 Combine the lime juice, vinegar, oil, garlic, and salt in a medium bowl. Transfer 3 tablespoons of the mixture to a zip-close plastic bag; add the chicken and chili powder. Squeeze out the air and seal the bag; turn to coat the chicken. Refrigerate, turning the bag occasionally, about 10 minutes. Set the remaining lime juice mixture in the bowl aside.

2 Spray the broiler rack with olive oil nonstick spray and preheat the broiler.

3 To make the salad, add the corn, zucchini, onion, cilantro, and cayenne to the reserved lime juice mixture in the bowl; toss to coat. Cover and refrigerate until ready to serve, at least 10 minutes or up to 1 day.

4 Remove the chicken from the marinade; discard the marinade. Thread the chicken onto 4 (8-inch) metal skewers. Broil 4 inches from the heat until lightly browned on the outside and cooked through, about 3½ minutes on each side. Serve the kebabs with the salad.

PER SERVING (1 kebab with ¾ cup salad): 232 Cal, 6 g Fat, 1 g Sat Fat, 0 g Trans Fat, 63 mg Chol, 357 mg Sod, 21 g Carb, 3 g Fib, 26 g Prot, 30 mg Calc. ***POINTS*** value: ***5.***

PLAY IT SAFE Since metal skewer handles become extremely hot, use tongs or oven mitts to turn them and to transfer the skewers to plates.

Peppered Chicken with Demi-Glace Sauce

HANDS-ON PREP **10 MIN**
COOK **15 MIN**
SERVES **4**

- **1½ teaspoons whole tri-color or black peppercorns**
- **4 (¼-pound) skinless boneless chicken breast halves**
- **¼ + ⅛ teaspoon salt**
- **3 teaspoons unsalted butter**
- **¼ cup finely chopped onion**
- **2 garlic cloves, minced**
- **⅓ cup dry white wine**
- **¾ cup prepared demi-glace**
- **1 tablespoon Dijon mustard**

1 Place the peppercorns in a zip-close plastic bag. With a meat mallet or the bottom of a heavy skillet, crack the peppercorns.
2 Sprinkle the chicken with the ¼ teaspoon salt. Press the cracked peppercorns onto both sides of each chicken breast half.
3 Melt 1 teaspoon of the butter in a large nonstick skillet over medium-high heat. Add the chicken and cook until browned and cooked through, 4–5 minutes on each side. Transfer the chicken to a serving plate; cover and keep warm.
4 Wipe out the skillet. Add 1 teaspoon of the butter and melt over medium-high heat. Add the onion and garlic; cook, stirring occasionally, until softened, about 1 minute. Add the wine and simmer until it is almost evaporated, about 2 minutes. Add the demi-glace and mustard; cook until the mixture begins to thicken slightly, about 3 minutes. Remove the skillet from the heat and swirl in the remaining 1 teaspoon butter and the ⅛ teaspoon salt. Serve the chicken at once with the sauce.

PER SERVING (1 chicken breast half with about 3 tablespoons sauce): 195 Cal, 7 g Fat, 3 g Sat Fat, 0 g Trans Fat, 76 mg Chol, 401 mg Sod, 4 g Carb, 1 g Fib, 26 g Prot, 30 mg Calc. ***POINTS*** value: ***4.***

TRY IT *Demi-glace* (DEHM-ee glahs) is an intensely flavored brown sauce that takes a while to cook from scratch. Fortunately, you can find prepared demi-glace in gourmet stores and in the meat department of some large supermarkets.

Grilled Chicken with Salsas

HANDS-ON PREP **10 MIN**
COOK **20 MIN**
SERVES **4**

- **½ cup prepared fat-free tomatillo salsa**
- **½ cup prepared hot, medium, or mild fat-free tomato salsa**
- **¼ cup finely chopped onion**
- **1 teaspoon grated orange zest**
- **⅛ teaspoon ground cumin**
- **4 (¼-pound) skinless boneless chicken breast halves**
- **4 cups shredded green or red cabbage, steamed**

1 Combine the salsas, onion, orange zest, and cumin in a zip-close plastic bag; add the chicken. Squeeze out the air and seal the bag; turn to coat the chicken. Refrigerate, turning the bag occasionally, about 20 minutes.

2 Remove the chicken from the marinade and scrape off the excess. Bring the marinade to a boil in a small saucepan; boil 2 minutes. Remove the saucepan from the heat and keep warm.

3 Spray a large ridged grill pan with canola nonstick spray and set over medium heat. Add the chicken and cook, turning occasionally, until cooked through, 10–12 minutes. Transfer to a cutting board. When cool enough to handle, using your fingers, shred the chicken or cut into long thin strips. Return the chicken to the cooked marinade in the saucepan, reheat gently, and serve over the cabbage.

PER SERVING (1 cup chicken mixture with about ½ cup cabbage): 169 Cal, 3 g Fat, 1 g Sat Fat, 0 g Trans Fat, 63 mg Chol, 408 mg Sod, 10 g Carb, 3 g Fib, 25 g Prot, 67 mg Calc. ***POINTS*** value: ***3.***

EXPRESS LANE Save time and don't steam the cabbage; simply serve the chicken mixture over crunchy, finely shredded raw cabbage, such as packaged coleslaw mix.

Chicken with Broccoli Rabe and Apple

HANDS-ON PREP **15 MIN**
COOK **20 MIN**
SERVES **4**

- **2 teaspoons olive oil**
- **1 large onion, chopped**
- **4 garlic cloves, minced**
- **1 pound chicken tenders**
- **1 bunch broccoli rabe, cleaned and chopped**
- **1 McIntosh apple, diced**
- **2½ teaspoons chicken bouillon granules**
- **¼ teaspoon crushed red pepper**
- **8 pitted brine-cured kalamata olives, chopped**

1 Heat the oil in a nonstick Dutch oven over medium-high heat. Add the onion and garlic; cook, stirring frequently, until golden, 7–10 minutes.

2 Add the chicken and cook, turning occasionally, until lightly browned, about 3 minutes. Add the broccoli rabe and the water that clings to its leaves, the apple, bouillon granules, and crushed red pepper; bring to a boil. Reduce the heat and simmer, covered, until the chicken is cooked through and the broccoli rabe is tender, about 8 minutes. Stir in the olives and serve at once.

PER SERVING (1⅓ cups): 237 Cal, 7 g Fat, 1 g Sat Fat, 0 g Trans Fat, 63 mg Chol, 456 mg Sod, 14 g Carb, 4 g Fib, 27 g Prot, 102 mg Calc. ***POINTS*** value: ***5.***

ZAP IT A leftover portion of this dish heats up beautifully in the microwave: Simply place in a microwavable bowl, cover with plastic wrap, turning back one corner to vent, and microwave on High until heated through, 3 minutes.

Chicken with White Beans and Rosemary

HANDS-ON PREP **20 MIN**
COOK **1 HR**
SERVES **4**

- **1 teaspoon olive oil**
- **1 large onion, chopped**
- **3 garlic cloves, minced**
- **3 carrots, chopped**
- **½ fennel bulb, trimmed and chopped**
- **1 tablespoon all-purpose flour**
- **1 (14½-ounce) can diced tomatoes**
- **½ cup reduced-sodium chicken broth**
- **¼ cup dry red wine**
- **2 bay leaves**
- **½ teaspoon salt**
- **¼ teaspoon coarsely ground black pepper**
- **4 (5–6-ounce) skinless bone-in chicken thighs**
- **1 (15½-ounce) can cannellini (white kidney) beans, rinsed and drained**
- **1 tablespoon finely chopped fresh rosemary, or 1 teaspoon dried**
- **2 teaspoons grated lemon zest**

1 Heat the oil in a nonstick Dutch oven over medium-high heat. Add the onion and garlic; cook, stirring occasionally, until golden, about 8 minutes. Add the carrots and fennel; cook, stirring occasionally, until crisp-tender, about 2 minutes.

2 Add the flour and cook, stirring constantly, until it browns slightly, about 1 minute. Add the tomatoes, broth, wine, bay leaves, salt, and pepper; bring to a boil, stirring constantly to scrape the browned bits from the bottom of the pot. Add the chicken. Reduce the heat and simmer, covered, until the chicken is cooked through and the vegetables are tender, about 40 minutes.

3 Add the beans, rosemary, and lemon zest to the pot; return to a boil. Reduce the heat and simmer, uncovered, stirring occasionally, until heated through, about 3 minutes. Discard the bay leaves before serving.

PER SERVING (1 chicken thigh with 1¼ cups bean mixture): 336 Cal, 9 g Fat, 3 g Sat Fat, 0 g Trans Fat, 57 mg Chol, 771 mg Sod, 34 g Carb, 9 g Fib, 29 g Prot, 116 mg Calc. ***POINTS*** value: ***7.***

GOOD IDEA Cook up a double batch of this satisfying family favorite; pack and freeze half up to 3 months for an easy meal another day.

CHICKEN WITH WHITE BEANS AND ROSEMARY

Spicy Cashew Chicken Stir-Fry

HANDS-ON PREP **10 MIN**
COOK **10 MIN**
SERVES **4**

- **¾ cup reduced-sodium chicken broth**
- **3 tablespoons + 2 teaspoons dry sherry**
- **3 tablespoons reduced-sodium soy sauce**
- **1 tablespoon + 2 teaspoons cornstarch**
- **1 tablespoon chili-garlic paste**
- **3 teaspoons peanut oil**
- **1 pound chicken tenders**
- **1 onion, chopped**
- **1 tablespoon grated peeled fresh ginger**
- **½ bunch broccoli, cut into florets (about 3 cups)**
- **¼ cup water**
- **¼ cup unsalted cashews, coarsely chopped**

1 Whisk together the broth, sherry, soy sauce, cornstarch, and chili-garlic paste in a bowl until smooth; set aside.

2 Heat a large nonstick skillet or wok over medium-high heat until a drop of water sizzles. Add 2 teaspoons of the oil, swirl to coat the pan, then add the chicken. Stir-fry until the chicken is cooked through, 4–5 minutes. Transfer the chicken to a plate; cover to keep warm.

3 Heat the remaining 1 teaspoon oil in the same skillet. Add the onion and ginger; stir-fry until fragrant, about 30 seconds. Add the broccoli; stir-fry until crisp-tender, about 2 minutes. Add the broth mixture and the water; cook, stirring constantly, until the mixture bubbles and thickens, about 1 minute. Add the chicken and cashews; cook until heated through, about 1 minute.

PER SERVING (1 cup): 288 Cal, 12 g Fat, 3 g Sat Fat, 0 g Trans Fat, 68 mg Chol, 588 mg Sod, 15 g Carb, 3 g Fib, 30 g Prot, 58 mg Calc. ***POINTS*** value: ***6.***

GOOD IDEA If you aren't a cashew fan, almonds or peanuts make a suitable substitute. Or, if you prefer, omit the nuts—you would reduce the per-serving ***POINTS*** value by 1.

Chicken Thigh Fricassee

HANDS-ON PREP **15 MIN**
COOK **45 MIN**
SERVES **4**

- **4 (5–6-ounce) skinless bone-in chicken thighs**
- **¾ teaspoon salt**
- **¼ teaspoon freshly ground pepper**
- **3 teaspoons extra-virgin olive oil**
- **2 onions, thinly sliced**
- **2 garlic cloves, minced**
- **¼ pound fresh shiitake mushrooms, stems discarded and caps sliced**
- **1 carrot, thinly sliced**
- **½ teaspoon dried thyme**
- **1 cup reduced-sodium chicken broth**

1 Sprinkle the chicken with the salt and pepper. Heat 1 teaspoon of the oil in a large nonstick skillet over medium-high heat. Add the chicken and cook until browned, 3–4 minutes on each side. Transfer the chicken to a plate.

2 Heat the remaining 2 teaspoons oil in the same skillet over medium heat. Add the onions and garlic; cook, stirring frequently, until golden, about 10 minutes. Add the mushrooms, carrot, and thyme; increase the heat and cook, stirring occasionally, until the carrot is crisp-tender, about 5 minutes. Reduce the heat and cook, stirring occasionally, until the vegetables are softened, 3–4 minutes. Stir in the broth; bring to a boil. Add the chicken; reduce the heat and simmer, covered, until cooked through, about 20 minutes.

PER SERVING (1 chicken thigh with ⅓ cup vegetables and sauce): 236 Cal, 11 g Fat, 3 g Sat Fat, 0 g Trans Fat, 57 mg Chol, 593 mg Sod, 10 g Carb, 2 g Fib, 22 g Prot, 46 mg Calc. ***POINTS*** value: ***5.***

CHICKEN AND SHRIMP GUMBO

Chicken and Shrimp Gumbo

HANDS-ON PREP **20 MIN**
COOK **45 MIN**
SERVES **6**

- **¼ pound spicy chicken sausage, casings removed**
- **1 onion, chopped**
- **1 green bell pepper, seeded and chopped**
- **1 red bell pepper, seeded and chopped**
- **2 tablespoons all-purpose flour**
- **1 (14½-ounce) can Cajun-style stewed tomatoes**
- **¾ cup reduced-sodium chicken broth**
- **¾ pound skinless boneless chicken thighs, cut into 1½-inch chunks**
- **1 teaspoon Cajun or seafood seasoning**
- **½ pound large shrimp, peeled and deveined**
- **1 (10-ounce) package frozen sliced okra**
- **2 cups fresh or frozen corn kernels**
- **1 tablespoon chopped fresh thyme, or 1 teaspoon dried**
- **2 cups hot cooked white rice**

1 Spray a nonstick Dutch oven with nonstick spray. Add the sausage and onion; cook, stirring with a wooden spoon to break up the sausage, until browned, about 10 minutes. Add the bell peppers and cook, stirring occasionally, until softened, about 6 minutes. Add the flour and cook, stirring constantly, until lightly browned, about 1 minute. Stir in the tomatoes and broth; bring to a boil, stirring constantly. Add the chicken and Cajun seasoning; return to a boil. Reduce the heat and simmer, covered, until the chicken is just cooked through, about 5 minutes.

2 Add the shrimp, okra, corn, and thyme; return to a boil. Reduce the heat and simmer, covered, until the shrimp are just opaque in the center, about 5 minutes. Serve at once with the rice.

PER SERVING (generous 1 cup gumbo with ⅓ cup rice): 321 Cal, 8 g Fat, 2 g Sat Fat, 0 g Trans Fat, 82 mg Chol, 734 mg Sod, 39 g Carb, 4 g Fib, 25 g Prot, 99 mg Calc. ***POINTS*** value: ***6.***

FOOD NOTE Traditional gumbos are frequently made with crab boil, a dry seasoning mix available in jars near the seafood section of most supermarkets. If you like, substitute 1 tablespoon crab boil (wrap it in a double layer of cheesecloth and tie it with kitchen string) for the Cajun seasoning, then discard the bag before serving the gumbo.

Chicken Meatballs in Tomato Pesto

HANDS-ON PREP **20 MIN**
COOK **20 MIN**
SERVES **4**

- **1 cup sun-dried tomatoes (not oil-packed)**
- **1 cup prepared sun-dried tomato pasta sauce**
- **1 cup fresh basil leaves**
- **2/3 cup cold water**
- **1 pound ground skinless chicken breast**
- **1/3 cup seasoned dried bread crumbs**
- **1/3 cup grated Parmesan cheese**
- **1 egg white**
- **1/4 teaspoon freshly ground pepper**
- **1 tablespoon olive oil**

1 Combine the sun-dried tomatoes and enough boiling water to cover in a bowl. Let stand until softened, about 10 minutes; drain.
2 Put the sun-dried tomatoes, pasta sauce, basil, and cold water in a blender and puree.
3 Combine the chicken, bread crumbs, cheese, egg white, and pepper in a large bowl until well mixed. Shape the mixture into 20 meatballs.
4 Heat the oil in a large nonstick skillet over medium heat. Add the meatballs and cook, turning occasionally, until browned, about 4 minutes. Add the sun-dried tomato mixture and bring to a boil. Reduce the heat and simmer, covered, until the meatballs are cooked through, about 7 minutes.

PER SERVING (5 meatballs with 1/3 cup sauce): 347 Cal, 12 g Fat, 4 g Sat Fat, 0 g Trans Fat, 75 mg Chol, 894 mg Sod, 27 g Carb, 3 g Fib, 33 g Prot, 190 mg Calc. ***POINTS*** value: ***7.***

GOOD IDEA Turn leftovers into a quick meatball sub: Fill a 2-ounce hero roll with 5 meatballs and 1/3 cup sauce, then top with 2 tablespoons shredded part-skim mozzarella cheese. Wrap the sandwich in foil and bake in a 350°F oven until the meatballs are thoroughly heated through and the cheese is melted, about 20 minutes. Cut the hero in half and serve as a hearty lunch for two with a per-serving ***POINTS*** value of 6.

Chicken Sausage and Cabbage Sauté

HANDS-ON PREP **15 MIN**
COOK **20 MIN**
SERVES **4**

- **6** ounces no-yolk egg noodles
- **2** teaspoons canola oil
- **1** (9-ounce) package fully-cooked smoked chicken-apple sausage, cut into 1-inch pieces
- **1** onion, thinly sliced
- **2** garlic cloves, minced
- **1** Granny Smith apple, peeled and cut into ¼-inch-thick slices
- **½** small head red cabbage, shredded (about 4 cups)
- **2½** tablespoons sugar
- **2** tablespoons apple-cider vinegar
- **½** teaspoon salt
- **¼** teaspoon caraway seeds
- **¼** teaspoon freshly ground pepper

1 Cook the noodles according to package directions omitting the salt, if desired.
2 Meanwhile, heat 1 teaspoon of the oil in a large nonstick skillet over medium-high heat. Add the sausage and cook, turning occasionally, until browned, about 4 minutes. Transfer the sausage to a plate.
3 Heat the remaining 1 teaspoon oil in the same skillet. Add the onion and garlic; cook, stirring frequently, until softened, about 3 minutes. Add the apple and cook, stirring occasionally, until softened, about 2 minutes. Add the cabbage, sugar, vinegar, salt, caraway seeds, and pepper; cook, stirring frequently, until the cabbage is wilted, about 5 minutes. Add the sausage and cook until heated through, about 1 minute. Serve with the noodles.

PER SERVING (1 cup noodles with 1 cup sausage mixture): 360 Cal, 9 g Fat, 2 g Sat Fat, 0 g Trans Fat, 33 mg Chol, 942 mg Sod, 54 g Carb, 4 g Fib, 16 g Prot, 62 mg Calc. ***POINTS*** value: ***7.***

FOOD NOTE There is a wide selection of flavored, reduced-fat cooked chicken sausages in large supermarkets and some specialty stores—keep a package in your freezer at the ready for recipes like this. If you can't find smoked chicken-apple sausage, try another flavor, plain chicken sausage, or reduced-fat turkey kielbasa instead.

Chicken-Stuffed Bell Peppers

HANDS-ON PREP **25 MIN**
COOK **1 HR 10 MIN**
SERVES **4**

6 tablespoons pearl barley, rinsed
1⅓ cups water
4 large red, green, or yellow bell peppers
1 small onion, chopped
1 celery stalk, chopped
¾ pound ground skinless chicken breast
1¼ cups light beer or reduced-sodium chicken broth
2 tablespoons Dijon mustard
½ teaspoon caraway seeds (optional)
½ teaspoon salt
Freshly ground pepper, to taste
3 tablespoons golden raisins
2 tablespoons sliced almonds

1 Combine the barley and water in a small saucepan; bring to a boil. Reduce the heat and simmer, covered, until tender, about 35 minutes. Remove the pan from the heat and let stand, covered, 10 minutes.

2 Meanwhile, cut ¼-inch off the tops of the bell peppers, then core and seed the bell peppers. Bring a large pot of water to a boil, add the bell peppers, and cook 3 minutes; drain. Rinse under cold running water; drain.

3 Preheat the oven to 375°F. To make the filling, spray a large skillet with nonstick spray and set over medium heat. Add the onion and celery; cook, stirring frequently, until softened, about 3 minutes. Add the chicken and cook, breaking it up with a wooden spoon, until browned, about 2 minutes. Add ¼ cup of the beer, the mustard, caraway seeds (if using), salt, and ground pepper. Cook, stirring occasionally, until the liquid reduces to a glaze, about 2 minutes. Remove the skillet from the heat and stir in the cooked barley, raisins, and almonds.

4 Stuff the filling into each bell pepper. Place the stuffed peppers in a 9-inch square baking dish. Pour the remaining 1 cup beer around the stuffed peppers. Bake until the peppers and filling are cooked through, about 30 minutes. Carefully transfer the stuffed peppers to 4 plates, using two large spoons and supporting the bottom of each pepper as you pick it up. Discard the sauce in the dish.

PER SERVING (1 stuffed pepper): 292 Cal, 5 g Fat, 1 g Sat Fat, 0 g Trans Fat, 51 mg Chol, 545 mg Sod, 35 g Carb, 7 g Fib, 24 g Prot, 60 mg Calc. ***POINTS*** value: ***5.***

CHICKEN-STUFFED BELL PEPPERS

Speedy Barbecue Chicken

HANDS-ON PREP **10 MIN**
COOK **20 MIN**
SERVES **4**

- **4** **ounces wagon-wheel pasta**
- **1** **tablespoon canola oil**
- **1** **onion, chopped**
- **2** **garlic cloves, minced**
- **1** **(14½-ounce) can diced tomatoes with green peppers and onions**
- **¼** **cup prepared barbecue sauce**
- **1** **teaspoon chili powder**
- **½** **(10-ounce) package carved roasted skinless chicken breast pieces, diced**
- **1** **cup fresh or frozen corn kernels**

1 Cook the pasta according to package directions omitting the salt, if desired.

2 Meanwhile, heat the oil in a large nonstick skillet over medium-high heat. Add the onion and garlic; cook, stirring frequently, until softened, about 3 minutes. Add the tomatoes, barbecue sauce, and chili powder; bring to a boil. Reduce the heat and simmer until the flavors are blended, about 2 minutes. Add the chicken and simmer, covered, stirring occasionally, until slightly thickened, about 10 minutes. Stir in the corn and cook until heated through, about 2 minutes. Serve with the pasta.

PER SERVING (¾ cup pasta with generous ½ cup chicken mixture): 297 Cal, 6 g Fat, 1 g Sat Fat, 0 g Trans Fat, 30 mg Chol, 476 mg Sod, 45 g Carb, 4 g Fib, 17 g Prot, 54 mg Calc. ***POINTS*** value: ***6.***

ZAP IT For the same ***POINTS*** value per serving, skip the pasta and turn any leftover barbecue chicken into sloppy Joes: Simply place ½ cup of the chicken mixture in a small microwavable bowl, cover with wax paper, and microwave on High until heated through, about 2 minutes. Spoon into a 2-ounce hamburger bun and top with sliced onions and dill pickles.

Chicken Fried Rice

HANDS-ON PREP **10 MIN**
COOK **10 MIN**
SERVES **4**

1 Whisk together the tomato paste and fish sauce in a small bowl until smooth; set aside.
2 Heat a large nonstick skillet or wok over medium-high heat until a drop of water sizzles. Add 1 teaspoon of the oil, swirl to coat the pan, then add the eggs. Stir-fry until firm, about 2 minutes. Transfer the scrambled eggs to a plate.
3 Heat the remaining 2 teaspoons oil in the same skillet. Add the onion and garlic; stir-fry until softened, about 3 minutes. Add the chicken and rice; stir-fry until the rice is coated, about 1 minute. Add the tomatoes and the tomato paste mixture; stir-fry until the tomatoes are softened, about 2 minutes. Remove the skillet from the heat; stir in the scrambled eggs and cilantro. Serve at once.

PER SERVING (1 cup): 257 Cal, 8 g Fat, 2 g Sat Fat, 0 g Trans Fat, 136 mg Chol, 529 mg Sod, 28 g Carb, 1 g Fib, 17 g Prot, 38 mg Calc. ***POINTS*** value: ***6.***

HOW WE DID IT When making this dish it is best to use rice that was cooked the day before and refrigerated (try rice from the Chinese take-out). Chilling dries out the rice and helps to keep the grains separated when stir-frying.

- **1 tablespoon tomato paste**
- **1 tablespoon Asian fish sauce (nam pla)**
- **3 teaspoons canola oil**
- **2 large eggs, lightly beaten**
- **1 onion, chopped**
- **2 garlic cloves, minced**
- **½ (10-ounce) package carved roasted skinless chicken breast pieces, diced**
- **2 cups cold cooked white rice**
- **2 plum tomatoes, seeded and cut into eighths**
- **1 tablespoon chopped fresh cilantro**

Chicken Tomatillo Casserole

HANDS-ON PREP **15 MIN**
COOK **40 MIN**
SERVES **4**

- **1** (7-ounce) can tomatillo sauce or 1 cup prepared salsa verde
- **1** cup fat-free sour cream
- **⅓** cup chopped fresh cilantro
- **1** large shallot, finely chopped
- **1** garlic clove, minced
- **8** fat-free corn tortillas
- **1½** cups shredded cooked chicken breast
- **¾** cup shredded fat-free Monterey Jack or cheddar cheese

1 Preheat the oven to 350°F. Spray a 2-quart shallow baking dish with nonstick spray.
2 Combine the tomatillo sauce, sour cream, cilantro, shallot, and garlic in a large bowl.
3 Place 4 tortillas in the bottom of the baking dish, overlapping as necessary to cover as much of the surface as possible. (You can cut them to fit, if necessary.) Spoon half the tomatillo mixture over the tortillas. Sprinkle the chicken evenly over the sauce; sprinkle ½ cup of the cheese over the chicken. Place the remaining 4 tortillas on top, then spoon on the remaining sauce, spreading it evenly to the sides. Top with the remaining ¼ cup cheese.
4 Cover the baking dish and bake 25 minutes. Uncover and bake until golden brown and bubbly, about 15 minutes. Let stand about 5 minutes before serving.

PER SERVING (¼ of casserole): 346 Cal, 4 g Fat, 2 g Sat Fat, 0 g Trans Fat, 48 mg Chol, 702 mg Sod, 46 g Carb, 4 g Fib, 30 g Prot, 476 mg Calc. ***POINTS*** value: ***6.***

TRY IT *Tomatillos* (tohm-ah-TEE-ohs) look like green tomatoes, but they're actually related to gooseberries—as you can tell when you see them fresh, with the papery hulls still attached. They're acidic yet sweet, highly prized in Mexican cooking, and a good contrast to the chicken in this creamy Southwestern casserole.

Chicken and Potatoes with Pickled Onions

HANDS-ON PREP **20 MIN**
COOK **1 HR 5 MIN**
SERVES **4**

- **1 small red onion, thinly sliced**
- **3 tablespoons apple-cider vinegar**
- **2 (10-ounce) baking potatoes, scrubbed**
- **2 tablespoons fresh lime juice**
- **1 tablespoon red-wine vinegar**
- **1 tablespoon extra-virgin olive oil**
- **½ teaspoon salt**
- **¼ teaspoon dried thyme**
- **⅛ teaspoon hot pepper sauce**
- **2 cups shredded cooked chicken**
- **1 cup grape tomatoes, halved**
- **¼ cup chopped fresh mint, cilantro, or parsley**

1 To make the pickled onions, combine the red onion and enough cold water to cover in a medium saucepan; bring to a boil. Reduce the heat and simmer 30 seconds; drain. Place the onion in a small bowl and add the apple-cider vinegar and 2 tablespoons cold water. Cover and refrigerate until ready to use, at least 1 hour. Drain before serving.
2 Preheat the oven to 400°F.
3 Prick the potatoes in several places with a fork, place on the middle rack in the oven. Bake until fork-tender, about 1 hour. Let cool slightly, then cut into ½-inch pieces.
4 Meanwhile combine the lime juice, red-wine vinegar, oil, salt, thyme, and pepper sauce in a large bowl. Add the warm potatoes, chicken, tomatoes, and mint; toss lightly to coat. Serve with the pickled onions.

PER SERVING (1¼ cups chicken mixture with 3 tablespoons pickled onions): 272 Cal, 8 g Fat, 2 g Sat Fat, 0 g Trans Fat, 53 mg Chol, 361 mg Sod, 28 g Carb, 3 g Fib, 21 g Prot, 35 mg Calc. ***POINTS*** value: ***6.***

GOOD IDEA Make extra pickled onions—they keep in the refrigerator up to 2 weeks—and serve with grilled pork chops, chicken cutlets, or fish steaks.

CHICKEN CHILI MOLE TACOS

Chicken Chili Mole Tacos

HANDS-ON PREP **15 MIN**
COOK **20 MIN**
SERVES **4**

- **1 teaspoon canola oil**
- **1 large onion, chopped**
- **2 garlic cloves, minced**
- **1 tablespoon unsweetened cocoa powder**
- **1 teaspoon ancho chili powder**
- **1 teaspoon ground cumin**
- **½ teaspoon cinnamon**
- **½ teaspoon salt**
- **½ teaspoon sugar**
- **½ teaspoon dried oregano**
- **1 (14½-ounce) can diced tomatoes**
- **1 (15½-ounce) can pinto beans, rinsed and drained**
- **1 cup chopped cooked chicken**
- **8 taco shells, heated**
- **2 cups shredded romaine lettuce**
- **½ cup shredded reduced-fat cheddar cheese**

1 Heat the oil in a nonstick Dutch oven over medium heat. Add the onion and garlic; cook, stirring frequently, until golden, about 7 minutes. Add the cocoa powder, chili powder, cumin, cinnamon, salt, sugar, and oregano; cook, stirring constantly, until fragrant, about 1 minute.
2 Add the tomatoes; bring to a boil. Reduce the heat and simmer, stirring occasionally, until the flavors are blended, about 8 minutes. Stir in the beans and chicken; return to a simmer and cook until heated through, about 3 minutes.
3 Spoon about ⅓ cup of the chili into each of the taco shells. Serve with the lettuce and cheese.

PER SERVING (2 tacos with ½ cup lettuce and 2 tablespoons cheese): 383 Cal, 12 g Fat, 3 g Sat Fat, 2 g Trans Fat, 33 mg Chol, 834 mg Sod, 49 g Carb, 12 g Fib, 24 g Prot, 250 mg Calc. ***POINTS*** value: ***8.***

HOW WE DID IT To heat and crisp the taco shells, place them on a baking sheet and heat in a 350°F oven about 5 minutes. If you like, serve with a fresh salsa of chopped tomatoes, red onion, and cilantro mixed with balsamic vinegar, salt, and pepper.

Mild Turkey Chili with Cilantro Cream

HANDS-ON PREP **15 MIN**
COOK **35 MIN**
SERVES **6**

1 teaspoon canola oil
1 large onion, chopped
3 garlic cloves, minced
2 zucchini, diced
2 teaspoons ground cumin
1 teaspoon ancho chili powder
1 (16-ounce) jar mild picante sauce
½ cup reduced-sodium chicken broth
1 pound skinless boneless turkey breast, cut into 1-inch pieces
1 (15½-ounce) can pinto beans, rinsed and drained
6 tablespoons fat-free sour cream
2 tablespoons chopped fresh cilantro

1 Heat the oil in a nonstick Dutch oven over medium-high heat. Add the onion and garlic; cook, stirring frequently, until golden, about 5 minutes. Add the zucchini, cumin, and chili powder; cook, stirring occasionally, until fragrant, about 2 minutes.
2 Stir in the picante sauce and broth; bring to a boil. Add the turkey; reduce the heat and simmer, partially covered, until the flavors are blended and the turkey is cooked through, about 20 minutes. Stir in the beans; return to a boil. Reduce the heat and simmer, uncovered, until heated through, about 3 minutes.
3 Combine the sour cream and cilantro in a small bowl. Serve the chili with the cilantro cream.

PER SERVING (generous 1 cup chili with 1 tablespoon cilantro cream): 228 Cal, 2 g Fat, 0 g Sat Fat, 0 g Trans Fat, 51 mg Chol, 465 mg Sod, 27 g Carb, 7 g Fib, 25 g Prot, 121 mg Calc. ***POINTS*** value: ***4.***

TRY IT *Ancho* (AHN-choh) chili powder is rich in flavor, but not very hot. You can find it in the gourmet section of the spice aisle. Or use regular chili powder, if you prefer. To make this gentle chili spicier, add extra chili powder or a few drops of hot pepper sauce.

Ginger Turkey Stir-Fry

HANDS-ON PREP **10 MIN**
COOK **10 MIN**
SERVES **4**

- **⅓ cup reduced-sodium chicken broth**
- **¼ cup sake**
- **3 tablespoons oyster sauce**
- **1 tablespoon cornstarch**
- **2 teaspoons reduced-sodium soy sauce**
- **4 teaspoons Asian (dark) sesame oil**
- **1 pound turkey breast cutlets, cut into 2 x ¼-inch strips**
- **1 carrot, cut into matchstick-thin strips**
- **3 scallions, cut into 1-inch pieces**
- **1 tablespoon grated peeled fresh ginger**

1 Whisk together the broth, sake, oyster sauce, cornstarch, and soy sauce in a small bowl until smooth.

2 Heat a large nonstick skillet or wok over medium-high heat until a drop of water sizzles. Add 2 teaspoons of the sesame oil, swirl to coat the pan, then add the turkey. Stir-fry until the turkey is browned and cooked through, about 4 minutes. Transfer the turkey to a plate.

3 Heat the remaining 2 teaspoons sesame oil in the same skillet. Add the carrot, scallions, and ginger; stir-fry until the carrot is crisp-tender, about 2 minutes. Add the turkey and the broth mixture. Cook, stirring constantly, until the mixture bubbles and thickens, about 1 minute.

PER SERVING (¾ cup): 204 Cal, 6 g Fat, 1 g Sat Fat, 0 g Trans Fat, 75 mg Chol, 514 mg Sod, 8 g Carb, 1 g Fib, 28 g Prot, 33 mg Calc. ***POINTS*** value: ***4.***

TRY IT *Sake* (SAH-kee) is a slightly sweet Japanese wine made from fermented rice. In Japan, sake is often used in cooking, but it is mostly served as a warm drink in small cups. You can substitute dry vermouth, sherry, or dry white wine for the sake, if you prefer.

Turkey Tetrazzini

HANDS-ON PREP **20 MIN**
COOK **40 MIN**
SERVES **4**

- **6** **ounces whole-wheat spaghetti**
- **½** **pound ground skinless lean turkey breast**
- **½** **pound fresh cremini or white button mushrooms, thinly sliced**
- **3** **scallions, thinly sliced**
- **1½** **tablespoons all-purpose flour**
- **2** **teaspoons finely chopped fresh sage**
- **¼** **teaspoon salt**
- **Freshly ground pepper, to taste**
- **1¼** **cups reduced-sodium chicken broth**
- **¼** **cup sweet vermouth**
- **6** **tablespoons fat-free sour cream**
- **4** **tablespoons shredded reduced-fat cheddar cheese**

1 Cook the spaghetti according to package directions omitting the salt, if desired. Drain and set aside.
2 Meanwhile, preheat the oven to 375°F. Spray a 1-quart baking dish with nonstick spray.
3 Spray a large nonstick skillet with nonstick spray and set over medium heat. Add the turkey and cook, breaking it up with a wooden spoon, until browned, about 4 minutes. With a slotted spoon, transfer the turkey to a large bowl.
4 Add the mushrooms and scallions to the same skillet; cook, stirring frequently, until the mushrooms give off their liquid and it reduces by half, about 4 minutes. Return the turkey to the skillet, then sprinkle in the flour, sage, salt, and pepper. Cook, stirring constantly, just until the flour is absorbed, about 30 seconds. Stir in the broth and vermouth; bring the mixture to a boil. Reduce the heat and simmer until slightly thickened, about 1 minute. Remove the skillet from the heat and stir in the sour cream until smooth. Add the pasta and 3 tablespoons of the cheese; mix well.
5 Transfer the turkey-pasta mixture to the baking dish; sprinkle with the remaining 1 tablespoon cheese. Bake until lightly browned and bubbly, about 20 minutes. Let stand about 5 minutes before serving.

PER SERVING (scant 1 cup): 277 Cal, 2 g Fat, 1 g Sat Fat, 0 g Trans Fat, 40 mg Chol, 419 mg Sod, 39 g Carb, 4 g Fib, 26 g Prot, 141 mg Calc. ***POINTS*** value: ***5.***

EXPRESS LANE To save a little time and work, buy the mushrooms already sliced and substitute ½ teaspoon dried sage for the fresh sage.

Turkey and Penne Casserole

HANDS-ON PREP **20 MIN**
COOK **50 MIN**
SERVES **8**

- **3 cups whole-wheat penne**
- **2 teaspoons olive oil**
- **1 pound ground skinless lean turkey breast**
- **1 large onion, chopped**
- **4 garlic cloves, minced**
- **1 (28-ounce) can whole tomatoes, drained then broken up**
- **3/4 teaspoon salt**
- **1/2 teaspoon freshly ground pepper**
- **2 tablespoons chopped fresh oregano, or 2 teaspoons dried**
- **1 cup part-skim ricotta cheese**
- **1 cup shredded part-skim mozzarella cheese**

1 Preheat the oven to 350°F. Spray a 9 x 13-inch baking dish with nonstick spray.
2 Cook the penne according to package directions omitting the salt, if desired. Drain and transfer to a large bowl.
3 Meanwhile, heat the oil in a nonstick Dutch oven over medium-high heat. Add the turkey and cook, breaking it up with a wooden spoon, until browned, about 8 minutes. Add the onion and garlic; cook, stirring occasionally, until softened, about 3 minutes. Stir in the tomatoes, salt, and pepper; cook, stirring occasionally, until the sauce thickens slightly, about 15 minutes. Stir in the oregano.
4 Add the turkey mixture to the penne; mix well. Stir in the ricotta and 1/2 cup of the mozzarella; transfer to the baking dish. Sprinkle with the remaining 1/2 cup mozzarella. Bake until heated through and lightly browned, about 25 minutes.

PER SERVING (about 1 1/4 cups): 306 Cal, 7 g Fat, 3 g Sat Fat, 0 g Trans Fat, 53 mg Chol, 474 mg Sod, 37 g Carb, 4 g Fib, 27 g Prot, 235 mg Calc. ***POINTS*** value: ***6.***

GOOD IDEA Prepare this family-style casserole ahead without baking it, cover with heavy-duty foil, and keep in the freezer up to 2 months. Defrost the casserole in the refrigerator overnight, then bake as directed, except add 15 to 20 minutes to the baking time.

Turkey and Hominy Chili

HANDS-ON PREP **20 MIN**
COOK **50 MIN**
SERVES **4**

2 teaspoons olive oil
1 large onion, chopped
2 garlic cloves, minced
1 pound ground skinless lean turkey breast
1 (14½-ounce) can diced tomatoes
1 (4-ounce) can chopped mild green chiles
½ (6-ounce) can tomato paste
2 teaspoons chipotle chili powder
2 teaspoons dried oregano
¼ teaspoon salt
1 (15-ounce) can hominy, drained
½ cup finely chopped red onion
6 radishes, shredded
¼ cup chopped fresh cilantro
¼ cup shredded fat-free Monterey Jack cheese

1 Heat the oil in a nonstick Dutch oven over medium heat. Add the onion and garlic; cook, stirring frequently, until golden, about 7 minutes. Add the turkey and cook, breaking it up with a wooden spoon, until browned, about 5 minutes.
2 Stir in the tomatoes, green chiles, tomato paste, chili powder, oregano, and salt; bring to a boil. Reduce the heat and simmer, partially covered, until the chili thickens slightly, about 30 minutes. Stir in the hominy and cook until heated through, about 3 minutes.
3 Meanwhile, combine the red onion, radishes, and cilantro in a small bowl. Divide the chili mixture among 4 bowls; sprinkle each evenly with the cheese, then the radish mixture.

PER SERVING (1½ cups chili with 1 tablespoon cheese and ⅓ cup radish mixture): 286 Cal, 4 g Fat, 1 g Sat Fat, 0 g Trans Fat, 75 mg Chol, 579 mg Sod, 29 g Carb, 7 g Fib, 34 g Prot, 167 mg Calc. ***POINTS*** value: ***5.***

EXPRESS LANE If you don't have time to simmer the chili 30 minutes as directed in step 2, just simmer it 5 minutes, then add a tablespoon or two of cornmeal to the mixture—it will thicken instantly.

TURKEY AND HOMINY CHILI

Turkey Shepherd's Pie

HANDS-ON PREP **20 MIN**
COOK **40 MIN**
SERVES **6**

- **1 large sweet potato, peeled and quartered**
- **1 large Yukon Gold potato, scrubbed and quartered**
- **¼ cup low-fat (1%) milk**
- **1¼ teaspoons salt**
- **2 teaspoons olive oil**
- **1 large onion, chopped**
- **2 carrots, diced**
- **1¼ pounds ground skinless lean turkey breast**
- **2 teaspoons finely chopped fresh thyme, or ¾ teaspoon dried**
- **¼ teaspoon freshly ground pepper**
- **2 tablespoons all-purpose flour**
- **1¼ cups reduced-sodium chicken broth**
- **¼ cup tomato paste**

1 Combine the potatoes and enough cold water to cover in a medium saucepan; bring to a boil. Reduce the heat and simmer, covered, until fork-tender, about 15 minutes. Drain and mash the potatoes with the milk and 1 teaspoon of the salt.
2 Meanwhile, preheat the oven to 425°F.
3 To make the filling, heat the oil in a 12-inch nonstick skillet over medium-high heat. Add the onion and carrots; cook until golden, about 7 minutes. Add the turkey, thyme, the remaining ¼ teaspoon salt, and the pepper; cook, breaking up the turkey with a wooden spoon, until browned, about 4 minutes. Sprinkle in the flour and cook, stirring constantly, just until the flour is absorbed, about 30 seconds. Stir in the broth and tomato paste; bring the mixture to a boil. Reduce the heat and simmer, stirring constantly, until slightly thickened, about 1 minute.
4 Transfer the filling to a 2-quart baking dish; top with the potato mixture and spread evenly with a fork, making a pattern with the tines. Bake until heated through, about 15 minutes.

PER SERVING (⅙ of casserole): 225 Cal, 2 g Fat, 1 g Sat Fat, 0 g Trans Fat, 62 mg Chol, 683 mg Sod, 24 g Carb, 3 g Fib, 26 g Prot, 49 mg Calc. ***POINTS*** value: ***4.***

EXPRESS LANE Use a hand-held electric mixer to mash the potatoes quickly. Simply cook the potatoes in a stainless steel saucepan, then drain and mash them in the same pan. An electric mixer would damage a nonstick pan.

Twice-Baked Potatoes with Turkey Bacon

HANDS-ON PREP **15 MIN**
COOK **1 HR 45 MIN**
SERVES **4**

- **4 (½-pound) baking potatoes, scrubbed**
- **6 slices turkey bacon, cut into ½-inch pieces**
- **½ cup fat-free milk**
- **¼ cup fat-free sour cream**
- **2 tablespoons chopped fresh chives, or 2 tablespoons chopped scallion, green part only**
- **1½ cups fresh small broccoli florets, or frozen florets, thawed**
- **¼ cup shredded reduced-fat cheddar cheese**

1 Preheat the oven to 350°F. Prick the potatoes in several places with a fork; place on the middle oven rack. Bake until fork-tender, about 1 hour 15 minutes. Transfer to a rack to cool, about 10 minutes (leave the oven on).

2 Meanwhile, to make the filling, heat a medium nonstick skillet over medium heat. Add the bacon and cook, stirring frequently, until crisp, about 3 minutes. Transfer to a plate lined with paper towels and drain.

3 Slice the top third off each potato lengthwise; reserve the tops. Scoop out the flesh from each potato, leaving a ⅛-inch-thick layer still in the shell. Transfer the potato flesh to a large bowl. Scoop the flesh from the potato tops and transfer to the bowl. Discard the potato top skins.

4 Add the milk, sour cream, and chives to the potato flesh; mix well until creamy. Stir in the broccoli and bacon. Stuff one-quarter of the filling into each of the potato shells, mounding in the center. Top each with 1 tablespoon of the cheese. Place the stuffed potatoes in a large baking dish and bake until heated through and the tops are golden brown, about 30 minutes.

PER SERVING (1 stuffed potato): 335 Cal, 8 g Fat, 3 g Sat Fat, 0 g Trans Fat, 25 mg Chol, 698 mg Sod, 51 g Carb, 5 g Fib, 15 g Prot, 159 mg Calc. ***POINTS*** value: ***7.***

MAKE IT CORE For hearty stuffed potatoes that are suitable for the **Core Plan**, just omit the bacon and substitute fat-free for the reduced-fat cheese.

STUFFED CORNISH HENS

Stuffed Cornish Hens

HANDS-ON PREP **15 MIN**
COOK **1 HR 15 MIN**
SERVES **4**

- **3 tablespoons maple syrup**
- **2 teaspoons melted unsalted butter**
- **1 (10-ounce) package frozen chopped spinach, thawed and squeezed dry**
- **1 large pear, peeled and chopped**
- **¼ cup chopped pecans**
- **2 tablespoons chopped red onion**
- **½ teaspoon salt**
- **¼ teaspoon ground nutmeg**
- **Freshly ground pepper, to taste**
- **2 (1¼-pound) Cornish game hens**

1 Preheat the oven to 350°F. Place a rack in a roasting pan.

2 Combine 2 tablespoons of the maple syrup and the melted butter in a small bowl until smooth; set aside.

3 To make the stuffing, combine the remaining 1 tablespoon maple syrup, the spinach, pear, pecans, red onion, salt, nutmeg, and pepper in a medium bowl. Spoon half the filling into the main cavity of each of the hens. Tie the legs together with kitchen string to seal the stuffing inside.

4 Place the hens on the rack in the roasting pan. Baste with some of the syrup and butter mixture. Bake, basting every 15 minutes with the syrup and butter mixture, until an instant-read thermometer inserted in a thigh registers 180°F, about 1 hour 15 minutes. (When there is no longer any syrup and butter mixture, continue to baste the hens with the pan juices.)

5 Transfer the hens to a carving board; let stand about 5 minutes. Cut each hen in half along the breastbone, so that each piece has a leg and thigh. Pour the pan juices into a measuring cup and skim off any fat. Serve the hens with the pan juices. Remove the skin before eating.

PER SERVING (½ stuffed hen with 2 teaspoons pan juices): 321 Cal, 12 g Fat, 3 g Sat Fat, 0 g Trans Fat, 138 mg Chol, 415 mg Sod, 22 g Carb, 4 g Fib, 32 g Prot, 108 mg Calc. ***POINTS*** value: ***7.***

EXPRESS LANE For easy cleanup, before placing the rack in the roasting pan, line the pan with foil.

CHAPTER SIX

STEAKS, CHOPS,

AND MORE

Spiced Pot Roast with Red Wine

HANDS-ON PREP **25 MIN**
COOK **3 HR 10 MIN**
SERVES **8**

- **1 (2-pound) beef bottom round roast, trimmed**
- **1 teaspoon salt**
- **¼ teaspoon freshly ground pepper**
- **2 teaspoons olive oil**
- **1½ cups unsweetened apple cider**
- **1 cup dry red wine**
- **8 garlic cloves, peeled**
- **2 star anise**
- **1 bay leaf**
- **4 medium white turnips, peeled and each cut into 6 wedges**
- **3 carrots, cut into 1-inch pieces**
- **3 medium red potatoes, scrubbed and each cut into 6 wedges**
- **2 onions, each cut into 6 wedges**

1 Preheat the oven to 350°F. Sprinkle the beef with the salt and pepper.

2 Heat the oil in a Dutch oven over medium-high heat. Add the beef and cook, turning frequently, until browned, about 8 minutes. Add the cider and wine, stirring to scrape any browned bits from the bottom of the pot. Add the garlic, star anise, and bay leaf; bring to a boil. Cover, transfer the pot to the oven, and bake 1 hour, turning the beef halfway through.

3 Stir in the turnips, carrots, potatoes, and onions. Cover and bake until the beef and vegetables are fork-tender, about 2 hours. Discard the bay leaf. Transfer the beef to a cutting board and let cool 10 minutes. Cut into 16 slices and serve with the vegetables and sauce.

PER SERVING (2 slices beef with about ½ cup vegetables and sauce): 332 Cal, 14 g Fat, 5 g Sat Fat, 1 g Trans Fat, 69 mg Chol, 394 mg Sod, 29 g Carb, 4 g Fib, 23 g Prot, 48 mg Calc. ***POINTS*** value: ***7.***

GOOD IDEA Pot roast is great party fare because it tastes even better when made ahead. Prepare the recipe as directed, cool completely, then cover and refrigerate up to 3 days. Serve with a side of egg noodles to help soak up all the fabulous sauce (½ cup cooked noodles will increase the per-serving ***POINTS*** value by 2).

SPICED POT ROAST
WITH RED WINE

Steak with Rice, Beans, and Plantains

HANDS-ON PREP **15 MIN**
COOK **1 HR 15 MIN**
SERVES **6**

- **1 (1½-pound) flank steak, trimmed and cut crosswise into 4 pieces**
- **1 onion, sliced**
- **1 (14½-ounce) can reduced-sodium beef broth**
- **¾ cup brown rice**
- **2 teaspoons olive oil**
- **1 onion, chopped**
- **3 garlic cloves, minced**
- **2 tomatoes, seeded and chopped**
- **1 teaspoon paprika**
- **½ teaspoon salt**
- **½ teaspoon freshly ground pepper**
- **1 (15-ounce) can black beans, heated through, then drained**
- **1 very ripe plantain, peeled and cut crosswise into 12 pieces**

1 Combine the steak, the sliced onion, and the broth in a large skillet; bring to a boil. Reduce the heat and simmer, covered, until the steak is fork-tender, about 1 hour. Remove the skillet from the heat; let the steak stand in the broth mixture until cool enough to handle, about 15 minutes.

2 Meanwhile, cook the rice according to package directions omitting the salt, if desired.

3 Transfer the steak to a cutting board; discard the sliced onion and all but ¼ cup of the cooking liquid. Set the ¼ cup cooking liquid aside. With two forks, shred the steak into small pieces.

4 Wipe out the skillet and heat 1 teaspoon of the oil over medium-high heat. Add the chopped onion and garlic; cook, stirring occasionally, until the onion begins to soften, 2–3 minutes. Add the shredded steak and cook, stirring occasionally, until browned, about 3 minutes. Add the tomatoes, paprika, salt, and pepper; cook, stirring occasionally, until the vegetables are softened, about 2 minutes. (If the mixture begins to look dry, add the reserved ¼ cup cooking liquid.) Transfer the mixture to a serving bowl and keep warm.

5 Wipe out the skillet and heat the remaining 1 teaspoon oil over medium heat. Add the plantain and cook, stirring frequently, until softened, about 5 minutes. Serve with the rice and beans.

PER SERVING (about ½ cup steak with about ½ cup rice, ¼ cup beans, and 2 pieces plantain): 392 Cal, 11 g Fat, 4 g Sat Fat, 0 g Trans Fat, 55 mg Chol, 611 mg Sod, 44 g Carb, 7 g Fib, 29 g Prot, 48 mg Calc. ***POINTS*** value: ***8.***

Marinated Flank Steak

HANDS-ON PREP **10 MIN**
COOK **10 MIN**
SERVES **4**

- **4 garlic cloves, minced**
- **1 medium shallot, minced**
- **3 tablespoons reduced-sodium soy sauce**
- **2 tablespoons red-wine vinegar**
- **1 teaspoon dried oregano**
- **½ teaspoon dried thyme**
- **1 (1-pound) flank steak, trimmed**
- **½ teaspoon salt**
- **¼ teaspoon freshly ground pepper**

1 Combine the garlic, shallot, soy sauce, vinegar, oregano, and thyme in a zip-close plastic bag; add the steak. Squeeze out the air and seal the bag; turn to coat the steak. Refrigerate, turning the bag occasionally, at least 4 hours or overnight.
2 Spray the broiler rack with canola nonstick spray and preheat the broiler.
3 Remove the steak from the marinade; discard the marinade. Sprinkle the steak with the salt and pepper, and place on the broiler rack. Broil the steak 5 inches from the heat until an instant-read thermometer inserted in the center of the steak registers 145°F for medium, about 5 minutes on each side. Transfer the steak to a cutting board and let stand about 5 minutes. Cut the steak on an angle against the grain into 12 slices.

PER SERVING (3 slices): 167 Cal, 9 g Fat, 4 g Sat Fat, 0 g Trans Fat, 48 mg Chol, 454 mg Sod, 1 g Carb, 0 g Fib, 19 g Prot, 9 mg Calc. ***POINTS*** value: ***4.***

FOOD NOTE Look for extra-lean cuts of iron-rich steak. Aside from flank steak, inexpensive top round or London Broil would be a good choice for this recipe. The cooking times will remain the same.

HOISIN BEEF WITH ASIAN SLAW

Hoisin Beef with Asian Slaw

HANDS-ON PREP **15 MIN**
COOK **10 MIN**
SERVES **4**

- **3** tablespoons hoisin sauce
- **2** garlic cloves, minced
- **2** teaspoons grated peeled fresh ginger
- **2** tablespoons + 1 teaspoon seasoned rice vinegar
- **4** (3-ounce) filets mignons, about 1¼ inches thick, trimmed
- **1** tablespoon Asian fish sauce (nam pla)
- **1** tablespoon sugar
- **½** medium head napa cabbage, shredded
- **1** carrot, shredded
- **½** small red bell pepper, seeded and thinly sliced
- **2** scallions, chopped

1 Combine the hoisin sauce, garlic, ginger, and the 1 teaspoon vinegar in a zip-close plastic bag; add the filets. Squeeze out the air and seal the bag; turn to coat the filets. Refrigerate, turning the bag occasionally, at least 2 hours or overnight.
2 Spray the broiler rack with nonstick spray and preheat the broiler.
3 Meanwhile, to make the slaw, combine the 2 tablespoons vinegar, the fish sauce, and sugar in a small bowl. Combine the cabbage, carrot, bell pepper, and scallions in a large bowl. Add the fish sauce mixture; toss to coat.
4 Remove the filets from the marinade; discard the marinade. Pat the filets dry with paper towels and place on the broiler rack. Broil the filets 5 inches from the heat until an instant-read thermometer inserted in the center of each filet registers 145°F for medium, about 4 minutes on each side. Serve at once with the slaw.

PER SERVING (1 filet with 1 cup slaw): 186 Cal, 6 g Fat, 2 g Sat Fat, 0 g Trans Fat, 43 mg Chol, 768 mg Sod, 17 g Carb, 2 g Fib, 17 g Prot, 83 mg Calc. ***POINTS*** value: ***4.***

EXPRESS LANE Save time making the slaw by substituting about 4 cups packaged coleslaw mix (from the supermarket's produce section) for the cabbage and carrot.

Steak Diane

HANDS-ON PREP **10 MIN**
COOK **10 MIN**
SERVES **4**

4 **(3-ounce) filets mignons, about 1 inch thick, trimmed**
½ **teaspoon salt**
¼ **teaspoon freshly ground pepper**
3 **teaspoons unsalted butter**
1 **medium shallot, minced**
⅓ **cup brandy**
1 **tablespoon Dijon mustard**
1 **teaspoon fresh lemon juice**
1 **teaspoon Worcestershire sauce**
1 **tablespoon chopped fresh chives (optional)**

1 Slightly flatten the filets with the palm of your hand to a ¾-inch thickness; sprinkle both sides with the salt and pepper.
2 Melt 2 teaspoons of the butter in a medium nonstick skillet over medium-high heat. Add the filets and cook until an instant-read thermometer inserted in the center of each filet registers 145°F for medium, 4–5 minutes on each side. Transfer the filets to a plate and keep warm.
3 Reduce the heat under the skillet to medium. Add the shallot and cook until softened, about 2 minutes. Stir in the brandy, mustard, lemon juice, and Worcestershire sauce; bring to a boil and cook until the flavors are blended, about 1 minute. Remove the skillet from the heat; swirl in the remaining 1 teaspoon butter and the chives (if using) until the butter is melted. Pour the sauce over filets and serve at once.

PER SERVING (1 filet with about 1½ tablespoons sauce): 151 Cal, 8 g Fat, 4 g Sat Fat, 0 g Trans Fat, 51 mg Chol, 433 mg Sod, 3 g Carb, 0 g Fib, 15 g Prot, 16 mg Calc. ***POINTS*** value: ***4.***

GOOD IDEA Serve our enlightened interpretation of this elegant entrée with a side of mashed potatoes (½ cup for each serving will increase the ***POINTS*** value by 2).

Tex-Mex Beef Kebabs

HANDS-ON PREP **20 MIN**
COOK **10 MIN**
SERVES **4**

- **2** **garlic cloves, minced**
- **2** **tablespoons white vinegar**
- **1** **jalapeño pepper, seeded and finely chopped (wear gloves to prevent irritation)**
- **1** **teaspoon dried oregano**
- **1** **teaspoon chili powder**
- **¼** **teaspoon cinnamon**
- **¾** **pound beef tenderloin, trimmed and cut into 16 chunks**
- **1** **red bell pepper, seeded and cut into 16 pieces**
- **1** **small red onion, cut into 8 wedges**
- **½** **teaspoon salt**
- **¼** **cup prepared barbecue sauce**

1 To make the marinade, combine the garlic, vinegar, jalapeño, oregano, chili powder, and cinnamon in a medium bowl. Add the beef and toss to coat. Cover and refrigerate at least 2 hours or up to 24 hours.

2 Spray the grill rack with olive oil nonstick spray; prepare the grill for a medium-hot fire.

3 Remove the beef from the marinade; discard the marinade. Alternately thread the beef, bell pepper, and red onion onto 4 (8-inch) metal skewers; sprinkle both sides evenly with the salt and lightly spray with olive oil nonstick spray. Place the kebabs on the grill rack and grill until well marked, 3–4 minutes on each side. Brush the kebabs with the barbecue sauce and grill until an instant-read thermometer inserted in a piece of beef registers 145°F for medium, about 1 minute.

PER SERVING (1 kebab): 150 Cal, 7 g Fat, 3 g Sat Fat, 0 g Trans Fat, 42 mg Chol, 458 mg Sod, 7 g Carb, 2 g Fib, 15 g Prot, 25 mg Calc. ***POINTS*** value: ***3.***

GOOD IDEA Keep a box of quick cooking, boil-in-the-bag brown rice in your pantry to cook in minutes and serve with dishes like this. A bowl of brown rice will help fill you in a healthy way *and* tame the heat of these spicy kebabs (½ cup cooked rice for each serving will increase the ***POINTS*** value by 2.)

Salsa Burgers

HANDS-ON PREP **10 MIN**
COOK **10 MIN**
SERVES **4**

- **¾ pound ground lean beef (7% or less fat)**
- **1 large egg**
- **3 tablespoons seasoned dried bread crumbs**
- **1 tablespoon canned chopped green chiles, drained**
- **1 small garlic clove, minced**
- **1 teaspoon dried basil**
- **¼ teaspoon chipotle chili powder**
- **½ teaspoon salt**
- **4 multi-grain hamburger buns**
- **4 thin slices red onion**
- **½ cup prepared fat-free salsa**

1 Combine the beef, egg, bread crumbs, chiles, garlic, basil, chili powder, and salt in a medium bowl. With damp hands, form the mixture into 4 (½-inch-thick) patties.
2 Spray a medium nonstick skillet with nonstick spray and set over medium-high heat. Add the patties and cook until an instant-read thermometer inserted in the side of each patty registers 160°F for medium, 5–6 minutes on each side.
3 Place the burgers in the buns with the red onion and salsa.

PER SERVING (1 burger with 1 slice onion and 2 tablespoons salsa): 281 Cal, 8 g Fat, 3 g Sat Fat, 1 g Trans Fat, 102 mg Chol, 923 mg Sod, 28 g Carb, 4 g Fib, 24 g Prot, 71 mg Calc. ***POINTS*** value: ***5.***

FOOD NOTE Ground beef can be very high in fat; look for extra-lean ground beef with either 7% or 5% fat, or substitute ground skinless lean turkey breast for the beef and cook until an instant-read thermometer inserted in the side of each patty registers 165°F, about 6 minutes on each side. (The per-serving ***POINTS*** value will remain the same.)

Noodles with Sweet-and-Spicy Meat Sauce

HANDS-ON PREP **15 MIN**
COOK **25 MIN**
SERVES **6**

- **½** **pound vermicelli or fideos**
- **¾** **pound ground lean beef (7% or less fat)**
- **1** **white onion, chopped**
- **2** **garlic cloves, minced**
- **1** **jalapeño pepper, seeded and finely chopped (wear gloves to prevent irritation)**
- **¾** **teaspoon ground cumin**
- **¼** **teaspoon cinnamon**
- **1** **(28-ounce) can whole peeled tomatoes, chopped**
- **¼** **cup tomato paste**
- **½** **teaspoon salt**
- **⅛** **teaspoon freshly ground pepper**
- **4** **teaspoons chopped fresh cilantro**
- **2** **tablespoons grated Parmesan cheese**

1 Cook the pasta according to package directions omitting the salt, if desired.
2 Meanwhile, heat a large nonstick skillet over medium-high heat. Add the beef and cook, breaking it up with a wooden spoon, until it begins to brown, 4–5 minutes. Add the white onion, garlic, and jalapeño; cook, stirring occasionally, until the onion begins to soften, 3–4 minutes. Add the cumin and cinnamon; cook, stirring constantly, until fragrant, about 30 seconds. Stir in the tomatoes, tomato paste, salt, and pepper; bring to a boil. Reduce the heat and simmer, stirring occasionally, until the sauce is thickened, about 15 minutes. Remove the skillet from the heat and stir in the cilantro. Serve with the pasta and the cheese.

PER SERVING (1 cup pasta with 1 cup sauce and 1 teaspoon cheese): 276 Cal, 5 g Fat, 2 g Sat Fat, 0 g Trans Fat, 39 mg Chol, 467 mg Sod, 39 g Carb, 4 g Fib, 21 g Prot, 84 mg Calc. ***POINTS*** value: ***5.***

MAKE IT CORE Want to try this dish but still stick to the **Core Plan**? Then substitute whole-wheat spaghetti for the vermicelli and omit the Parmesan cheese.

Meatloaf with Caramelized Onions and Mushrooms

HANDS-ON PREP **10 MIN**
COOK **1 HR**
SERVES **6**

- **2** **teaspoons extra-virgin olive oil**
- **1** **large onion, chopped**
- **3** **garlic cloves, minced**
- **2** **teaspoons sugar**
- **½** **pound fresh mushrooms, sliced**
- **1½** **pounds ground lean beef (7% or less fat)**
- **1** **cup tomato sauce**
- **½** **cup plain dried bread crumbs**
- **2** **egg whites, lightly beaten**
- **1** **teaspoon dried basil**
- **1** **teaspoon salt**
- **¼** **teaspoon freshly ground pepper**
- **Ketchup (optional)**

1 Preheat the oven to 350°F. Spray a large rimmed baking sheet with nonstick spray.

2 Meanwhile, heat 1 teaspoon of the oil in a medium nonstick skillet over medium-high heat. Add the onion, garlic, and sugar; cook, stirring occasionally, until golden, about 10 minutes. Transfer to a large bowl. Heat the remaining 1 teaspoon oil in the same skillet. Add the mushrooms and cook, stirring occasionally, until browned, 6–7 minutes. Add to the bowl with the onion; let cool 5 minutes.

3 Stir in the beef, ½ cup of the tomato sauce, the bread crumbs, egg whites, basil, salt, and pepper until well combined.

4 Transfer the mixture to the baking sheet and form into a 4 x 9-inch loaf. Spread the remaining ½ cup tomato sauce over the top. Bake until an instant-read thermometer inserted in the center of the loaf registers 160°F, 45–55 minutes. Transfer the meatloaf to a cutting board and let stand about 10 minutes. Cut into 6 slices and serve with ketchup (if using).

PER SERVING (1 slice): 243 Cal, 8 g Fat, 3 g Sat Fat, 1 g Trans Fat, 62 mg Chol, 783 mg Sod, 16 g Carb, 2 g Fib, 28 g Prot, 49 mg Calc. ***POINTS*** value: ***5.***

GOOD IDEA Meatloaf makes terrific leftovers, so double the recipe and shape the mixture into 2 loaves (they'll both bake perfectly on the same baking sheet). Let the extra meatloaf cool, then wrap and refrigerate up to 3 days or freeze up to 2 months.

MEATLOAF WITH CARAMELIZED ONIONS AND MUSHROOMS; SESAME BROCCOLI, PAGE 267

FRUIT-STUFFED PORK LOIN

Fruit-Stuffed Pork Loin

HANDS-ON PREP **35 MIN**

COOK **1 HR 15 MIN**

SERVES **6**

- **2/3 cup port wine**
- **1/2 cup dried apricots, chopped**
- **1/2 cup dried pitted plums, chopped**
- **1/2 cup apricot preserves**
- **2 tablespoons plain dried bread crumbs**
- **1 tablespoon Dijon mustard**
- **1 (1 1/2-pound) boneless center-cut pork loin, trimmed**
- **1 teaspoon salt**
- **1/4 teaspoon freshly ground pepper**
- **1 onion, chopped**
- **1 carrot, chopped**
- **1 (14 1/2-ounce) can reduced-sodium beef broth**
- **1 tablespoon unsalted butter**

1 Preheat the oven to 400°F. Place a rack in a roasting pan and spray the rack and the pan with nonstick spray.

2 Stuffing: Bring the port, 1/4 cup of the apricots, and 1/4 cup of the plums to a simmer in a small saucepan over medium-high heat. Remove from the heat. Let stand until the fruits soften, about 10 minutes. Strain the fruits through a sieve, reserving the port liquid and transfer the fruits to a bowl. Combine the fruit with 1/4 cup of the preserves, the bread crumbs, and mustard; mix well.

3 Cut the pork in half lengthwise, leaving a 1/2-inch hinge (do not cut all the way through). Open up like a book. Place the pork, cut-side down, between 2 sheets of plastic wrap. Pound the pork 1/2-inch thick; sprinkle with 3/4 teaspoon of the salt and the pepper. Turn the pork, spoon the stuffing down the center, leaving a 1/2-inch border. Fold the pork over the filling and tie with kitchen string.

4 Place the onion, carrot, broth, and the reserved port liquid in the pan. Place the pork on the rack and roast 45 minutes. Brush the pork with 1 tablespoon of the preserves and roast 5 minutes. Repeat roasting and brushing the pork 3 more times with the remaining 3 tablespoons preserves until an instant-read thermometer inserted in center registers 160°F, about 15 minutes. Let stand 10 minutes.

5 Strain the pan juices through a sieve into a small saucepan. Discard the solids. Add the remaining 1/4 cup apricots and 1/4 cup plums; bring to a boil. Boil 1 minute. Remove the pan from the heat; swirl in the butter and the remaining 1/4 teaspoon salt. Cut the pork into 12 slices and serve with the sauce.

PER SERVING (2 slices pork with 3 tablespoons sauce): 334 Cal, 10 g Fat, 4 g Sat Fat, 0 g Trans Fat, 68 mg Chol, 668 mg Sod, 37 g Carb, 3 g Fib, 25 g Prot, 55 mg Calc. ***POINTS*** value: ***7.***

Spiced Roast Pork

HANDS-ON PREP **15 MIN**
COOK **1 HR 10 MIN**
SERVES **6**

- **1 (1½-pound) boneless center-cut pork loin, trimmed**
- **¼ cup chopped fresh parsley**
- **2 tablespoons apple-cider vinegar**
- **3 garlic cloves, minced**
- **1 tablespoon paprika**
- **2 teaspoons grated lime zest**
- **1 teaspoon cinnamon**
- **1 teaspoon ground cumin**
- **1 teaspoon salt**
- **½ teaspoon freshly ground pepper**

1 Pat the pork dry with paper towels. Combine the parsley, vinegar, garlic, paprika, lime zest, cinnamon, cumin, salt, and pepper in a large bowl. Add the pork and toss to coat. Cover and refrigerate at least 8 hours or up to 24 hours.

2 Preheat the oven to 325°F. Place a rack in a roasting pan and spray the rack and the pan with canola nonstick spray.

3 Place the pork on the rack and roast until an instant-read thermometer inserted in the center of the pork registers 160°F for medium, about 1 hour 10 minutes. Transfer the pork to a cutting board and let stand about 5 minutes. Cut into 12 slices.

PER SERVING (2 slices): 175 Cal, 8 g Fat, 3 g Sat Fat, 0 g Trans Fat, 64 mg Chol, 435 mg Sod, 2 g Carb, 1 g Fib, 23 g Prot, 29 mg Calc. ***POINTS*** value: ***4.***

GOOD IDEA Serve this fragrant roast with a side of beta carotene-rich mashed sweet potatoes (2/3 cup cooked potatoes for each serving will increase the ***POINTS*** value by 2).

Pork and Hominy Stew

HANDS-ON PREP **20 MIN**
COOK **45 MIN**
SERVES **6**

- **1 large onion, chopped**
- **½ cup packed fresh cilantro leaves**
- **½ cup water**
- **4 garlic cloves, peeled**
- **1 teaspoon dried oregano**
- **¾ teaspoon ground cumin**
- **2 teaspoons olive oil**
- **1½ pounds boneless pork loin, trimmed and cut into 1-inch pieces**
- **¾ teaspoon salt**
- **3 carrots, cut into 1-inch pieces**
- **1 (14½-ounce) can reduced-sodium chicken broth**
- **1 (15-ounce) can yellow or white hominy, rinsed and drained**

1 Puree the onion, cilantro, water, garlic, oregano, and cumin in a blender; set aside.

2 Heat the oil in a nonstick Dutch oven over medium-high heat. Add the pork and ½ teaspoon of the salt; cook, stirring occasionally, until browned, about 4 minutes. Add the carrots and cook, stirring occasionally, until they begin to soften, about 2 minutes. Add the reserved onion mixture and the broth; bring to a boil. Reduce the heat and simmer, partially covered, until pork and carrots are fork-tender, about 30 minutes. Stir in the hominy and the remaining ¼ teaspoon salt; cook until heated through, about 2 minutes.

PER SERVING (scant 1 cup): 225 Cal, 7 g Fat, 2 g Sat Fat, 0 g Trans Fat, 56 mg Chol, 586 mg Sod, 14 g Carb, 3 g Fib, 25 g Prot, 34 mg Calc. ***POINTS*** value: ***4.***

GOOD IDEA Make double the amount of this stew; pack and freeze half up to 3 months for a quick dinner another day. Remember to thaw the stew in the refrigerator the night before or defrost in the microwave at 30 percent power, 6 to 8 minutes, then reheat thoroughly in a saucepan.

Grilled Pork Tenderloin with Corn Relish

HANDS-ON PREP **15 MIN**
COOK **35 MIN**
SERVES **4**

- **3 garlic cloves**
- **2 teaspoons grated orange zest**
- **1 teaspoon olive oil**
- **1 (1-pound) pork tenderloin, trimmed**
- **2 slices bacon, chopped**
- **1 onion, chopped**
- **1½ cups frozen corn kernels**
- **2 teaspoons sugar**
- **1 tablespoon apple-cider vinegar**
- **1 tablespoon chopped fresh basil**
- **¾ teaspoon salt**
- **¼ teaspoon freshly ground pepper**

1 Mince 2 of the garlic cloves; transfer to a large bowl. Stir in the orange zest and oil. Add the pork and toss to coat. Cover and refrigerate at least 1 hour or up to 24 hours.

2 Meanwhile, to make the relish, mince the remaining 1 garlic clove. Spray a medium nonstick skillet with nonstick spray and set over medium-high heat. Add the bacon and cook, stirring occasionally, until crisp, 3–4 minutes. Add the remaining garlic and the onion; cook, stirring frequently, until the onion begins to soften, 2–3 minutes. Add the corn and sugar; cook, stirring occasionally, until the mixture begins to brown, 5–6 minutes. Stir in the vinegar and cook until evaporated, about 30 seconds. Remove the skillet from the heat; stir in the basil, ¼ teaspoon of the salt, and the pepper.

3 Spray the grill rack with nonstick spray; prepare the grill for a medium-hot fire.

4 Sprinkle the pork with the remaining ½ teaspoon salt. Place the pork on the grill rack and grill, turning occasionally, until an instant-read thermometer inserted in the center of the pork registers 160°F, about 25 minutes. Transfer the pork to a cutting board and let stand 5 minutes. Cut into 12 slices and serve with the relish.

PER SERVING (3 slices pork with about ⅓ cup relish): 235 Cal, 7 g Fat, 2 g Sat Fat, 0 g Trans Fat, 66 mg Chol, 535 mg Sod, 18 g Carb, 2 g Fib, 26 g Prot, 23 mg Calc. ***POINTS*** value: ***5.***

FOOD NOTE If you like, perk up the nutrition (and color) of the corn relish by adding some seeded and chopped red bell peppers or halved cherry tomatoes.

Grilled Korean-Style Pork

HANDS-ON PREP **15 MIN**
COOK **10 MIN**
SERVES **4**

- **1 (1-pound) pork tenderloin, trimmed**
- **3 garlic cloves, minced**
- **2 tablespoons honey**
- **2 tablespoons reduced-sodium soy sauce**
- **1 tablespoon grated peeled fresh ginger**
- **1 tablespoon seasoned rice vinegar**
- **2 teaspoons Asian (dark) sesame oil**
- **2 teaspoons chili-garlic paste**
- **½ teaspoon salt**

1 Cut the pork in half lengthwise, leaving a ½-inch hinge (do not cut all the way through). Open the pork up like a book. Place the pork, cut-side down, between 2 sheets of plastic wrap. Pound the pork to a ¾-inch thickness.

2 Combine the garlic, honey, soy sauce, ginger, vinegar, sesame oil, and chili-garlic paste in a large zip-close plastic bag; add the pork. Squeeze out the air and seal the bag; turn to coat the pork. Refrigerate the pork, turning the bag occasionally, at least 2 hours or overnight.

3 Spray the grill rack with nonstick spray; prepare the grill for a medium-hot fire.

4 Remove the pork from the marinade; discard the marinade. Sprinkle the pork with the salt. Place the pork on the grill rack and grill until well marked and an instant-read thermometer inserted in the center of the pork registers 160°F for medium, 5–6 minutes on each side. Transfer the pork to a cutting board and let stand about 5 minutes. Cut into 8 slices.

PER SERVING (2 slices): 166 Cal, 6 g Fat, 2 g Sat Fat, 0 g Trans Fat, 75 mg Chol, 163 mg Sod, 3 g Carb, 0 g Fib, 25 g Prot, 5 mg Calc. ***POINTS*** value: ***4.***

TRY IT Chili-garlic paste is a spicy Chinese condiment made from hot peppers, salt, and garlic. If you can't find it at the supermarket or Asian specialty store, substitute 1 jalapeño pepper, seeded and minced (wear gloves to prevent irritation) and 2 teaspoons ketchup.

PORK CHOPS IN TOMATO SAUCE

Pork Chops in Tomato Sauce

HANDS-ON PREP **15 MIN**
COOK **15 MIN**
SERVES **4**

- **4 garlic cloves**
- **3 tablespoons red-wine vinegar**
- **4 teaspoons extra-virgin olive oil**
- **1 teaspoon dried oregano**
- **1 teaspoon dried basil**
- **4 (¼-pound) boneless center-cut pork loin chops, trimmed**
- **½ teaspoon salt**
- **1 onion, chopped**
- **1 green bell pepper, seeded and chopped**
- **1 (8-ounce) can tomato sauce**

1 Mince 3 of the garlic cloves; transfer to a large bowl. Stir in the vinegar, 2 teaspoons of the oil, the oregano, and basil. Add the pork and toss to coat. Marinate at room temperature 30 minutes.

2 Remove the pork from the marinade; discard the marinade. Pat the pork dry with paper towels and sprinkle with the salt. Heat 1 teaspoon of the oil in a large nonstick skillet over medium-high heat. Add the pork and cook until browned, about 3 minutes on each side. Transfer the pork to a plate and set aside.

3 Mince the remaining 1 garlic clove. Heat the remaining 1 teaspoon oil in the same skillet over medium-high heat. Add the onion, bell pepper, and garlic; cook until the vegetables begin to soften, about 3 minutes. Add the tomato sauce and the reserved pork; turn the pork to coat with the sauce. Reduce the heat and simmer until an instant-read thermometer inserted in the side of each chop registers 160°F for medium, about 5 minutes.

PER SERVING (1 pork chop with ¼ cup sauce): 239 Cal, 12 g Fat, 4 g Sat Fat, 0 g Trans Fat, 51 mg Chol, 667 mg Sod, 11 g Carb, 2 g Fib, 22 g Prot, 42 mg Calc. ***POINTS*** value: ***5.***

GOOD IDEA Pair the chops with some roasted red potatoes for a hearty meal (1 cup cooked potatoes for each serving will increase the ***POINTS*** value by 2).

Skillet Pork with Tomatoes and Bell Pepper

HANDS-ON PREP **15 MIN**
COOK **10 MIN**
SERVES **4**

- **3 teaspoons canola oil**
- **1 pound pork tenderloin, trimmed and cut into ¾-inch pieces**
- **½ teaspoon salt**
- **1 onion, chopped**
- **1 green bell pepper, seeded and chopped**
- **2 garlic cloves, minced**
- **2 tomatoes, seeded and chopped**
- **½ cup reduced-sodium chicken broth**
- **1 tablespoon chopped fresh cilantro**
- **2 teaspoons fresh lime juice**

1 Heat 2 teaspoons of the oil in a large nonstick skillet over medium-high heat. Add the pork and ¼ teaspoon of the salt; cook, stirring occasionally, until browned, about 4 minutes. Transfer the pork to a medium bowl and set aside.
2 Heat the remaining 1 teaspoon oil in the same skillet over medium-high heat. Add the onion, bell pepper, and garlic; cook, stirring occasionally, until the vegetables begin to soften, about 2 minutes. Add the tomatoes and cook until softened, about 1 minute. Add the reserved pork and the broth; bring to a boil. Cook until the pork is cooked through, 2–3 minutes. Remove the skillet from the heat; stir in the cilantro, lime juice, and the remaining ¼ teaspoon salt. Serve at once.

PER SERVING (¾ cup): 206 Cal, 8 g Fat, 2 g Sat Fat, 0 g Trans Fat, 63 mg Chol, 422 mg Sod, 10 g Carb, 2 g Fib, 24 g Prot, 23 mg Calc. ***POINTS*** value: ***4.***

GOOD IDEA This dish would be ideal served with brown rice (½ cup cooked rice for each serving will increase the ***POINTS*** value by 2), but if you're looking for a switch from brown rice, keep a box of high-fiber bulgur on hand to serve with this simple sauté (½ cup cooked bulgur will increase the ***POINTS*** value by 1).

Asian Pork and Broccoli

HANDS-ON PREP **10 MIN**
COOK **10 MIN**
SERVES **4**

- **3 tablespoons dry sherry**
- **2 tablespoons reduced-sodium soy sauce**
- **2 tablespoons cornstarch**
- **1 cup reduced-sodium chicken broth**
- **1 tablespoon sugar**
- **1 pound pork tenderloin, trimmed and cut into ½-inch pieces**
- **3 teaspoons Asian (dark) sesame oil**
- **3 cups fresh broccoli florets**
- **3 garlic cloves, minced**
- **1 tablespoon grated peeled fresh ginger**
- **3 scallions, chopped**

1 Whisk together 2 tablespoons of the sherry, 1 tablespoon of the soy sauce, 1 tablespoon of the cornstarch, the broth, and sugar in a small bowl until smooth; set aside.

2 Combine the pork, the remaining 1 tablespoon sherry, 1 tablespoon soy sauce, and 1 tablespoon cornstarch in a medium bowl.

3 Heat 1½ teaspoons of the sesame oil in a large nonstick skillet over medium-high heat. Add the pork mixture and cook, stirring occasionally, until browned, 4–5 minutes; transfer to a plate.

4 Heat the remaining 1½ teaspoons sesame oil in the same skillet. Add the broccoli and cook, stirring constantly, until it turns dark green, about 1 minute. Add the garlic and ginger; cook, stirring frequently, until fragrant and beginning to brown, about 1 minute. Stir in the pork mixture and cook, stirring frequently, until the flavors are blended, about 1 minute. Stir in the reserved broth mixture; bring to a boil. Cook, stirring frequently, until the sauce thickens and coats the pork and broccoli, 1–2 minutes. Remove the skillet from the heat; stir in the scallions and serve at once.

PER SERVING (1 cup): 239 Cal, 9 g Fat, 2 g Sat Fat, 0 g Trans Fat, 75 mg Chol, 526 mg Sod, 12 g Carb, 2 g Fib, 28 g Prot, 41 mg Calc. ***POINTS*** value: ***5.***

GOOD IDEA Buy a large bag of fresh broccoli florets and steam the extra broccoli to have on hand to prepare an instant side dish, to pump up the nutrition of your favorite pasta, or just for snacking. Refrigerate cooked broccoli in a zip-close plastic bag up to 3 days.

Rosemary-Balsamic Veal Chops

HANDS-ON PREP **10 MIN**
COOK **15 MIN**
SERVES **4**

- **4 (6-ounce) bone-in veal chops, about ½ inch thick, trimmed**
- **¾ teaspoon chopped fresh rosemary, or ½ teaspoon dried**
- **½ teaspoon salt**
- **⅛ teaspoon freshly ground pepper**
- **3 teaspoons unsalted butter**
- **1 medium shallot, chopped**
- **¾ cup reduced-sodium beef broth**
- **2 tablespoons balsamic vinegar**
- **1 tablespoon honey**

1 Sprinkle the veal with the rosemary, salt, and pepper. Melt 2 teaspoons of the butter in a large nonstick skillet over medium-high heat. Add the veal and cook until browned and an instant-read thermometer inserted in the side of each chop registers 160°F for medium, 3–4 minutes on each side. Transfer to a plate.

2 Melt the remaining 1 teaspoon butter in the same skillet. Add the shallot and cook, stirring occasionally, until it begins to soften, about 1 minute. Add the broth, vinegar, and honey, stirring to scrape any browned bits from the bottom of the skillet. Bring to a boil and cook until slightly syrupy, about 5 minutes. Add the veal and cook, turning once, until heated through, about 1 minute. Serve at once.

PER SERVING (1 veal chop with 2 teaspoons sauce): 188 Cal, 8 g Fat, 3 g Sat Fat, 0 g Trans Fat, 83 mg Chol, 429 mg Sod, 6 g Carb, 0 g Fib, 21 g Prot, 25 mg Calc. ***POINTS*** value: ***4.***

GOOD IDEA Consider serving these succulent chops with a side of nutty-tasting wild rice (⅔ cup cooked wild rice for each serving will increase the ***POINTS*** value by 2).

Ham Steak with Pepper Jelly Glaze

HANDS-ON PREP **5 MIN**
COOK **10 MIN**
SERVES **4**

- **¼ cup hot pepper jelly**
- **2 teaspoons Dijon mustard**
- **1 teaspoon honey**
- **1 teaspoon apple-cider vinegar**
- **1 (1-pound) bone-in reduced-sodium ham steak, ½ inch thick**

1 Spray a broiler pan with nonstick spray and preheat the broiler.
2 Meanwhile, to make the glaze, combine the jelly, mustard, honey, and vinegar in a small bowl.
3 Place the ham on the broiler rack. Broil the ham 5 inches from the heat until beginning to brown, about 5 minutes. Brush with one-third of the glaze; broil 2 minutes. Repeat. Brush the ham with the remaining glaze and broil until heated through and the glaze is thickened and bubbly, about 2 minutes. Transfer the ham to a cutting board and let cool slightly before serving, about 2 minutes.

PER SERVING (¼ of ham steak with about 1 tablespoon glaze): 154 Cal, 3 g Fat, 1 g Sat Fat, 0 g Trans Fat, 36 mg Chol, 775 mg Sod, 18 g Carb, 0 g Fib, 14 g Prot, 11 mg Calc. ***POINTS*** value: ***3.***

GOOD IDEA Double the recipe and broil an extra ham steak for another meal or two. Cool the spare ham steak, then wrap and refrigerate up to 3 days. Dice the leftovers and stir into pasta, soups, or rice dishes.

Smothered Lamb Stew

HANDS-ON PREP **15 MIN**
COOK **40 MIN**
SERVES **4**

- **1 pound boneless leg of lamb, trimmed and cut into 1-inch pieces**
- **1 onion, chopped**
- **3 garlic cloves, minced**
- **¾ pound red potatoes, scrubbed and cut into 1-inch chunks**
- **2 carrots, cut into 1-inch chunks**
- **1 tablespoon paprika**
- **1 teaspoon dried oregano**
- **1 (14½-ounce) can reduced-sodium beef broth**
- **1 tablespoon red-wine vinegar**
- **1 bay leaf**

1 Spray a nonstick Dutch oven with canola nonstick spray and set over medium-high heat. Add the lamb and cook, turning frequently, until browned, about 5 minutes. Transfer the lamb to a medium bowl and set aside.

2 Add the onion and garlic to the same Dutch oven; cook, stirring frequently, until the onion begins to soften, 2–3 minutes. Add the potatoes, carrots, paprika, and oregano; cook, stirring constantly, until fragrant, about 30 seconds. Add the reserved lamb, the broth, vinegar, and bay leaf; bring to a boil. Reduce the heat and simmer, covered, until the lamb and vegetables are tender, 30–35 minutes. Discard the bay leaf before serving.

PER SERVING (1¼ cups): 263 Cal, 6 g Fat, 2 g Sat Fat, 0 g Trans Fat, 65 mg Chol, 271 mg Sod, 26 g Carb, 4 g Fib, 26 g Prot, 45 mg Calc. ***POINTS*** value: ***5.***

GOOD IDEA While you are preparing the carrots for this stew, cut a few extra into sticks for a healthy snack to tote to the office.

Classic Shepherd's Pie

HANDS-ON PREP **25 MIN**
COOK **50 MIN**
SERVES **6**

- **1½ pounds baking potatoes, peeled and cut into 1-inch pieces**
- **1 (½-pound) parsnip, peeled and cut into 1-inch pieces**
- **½ cup fat-free milk**
- **1 tablespoon unsalted butter**
- **1 teaspoon salt**
- **¼ teaspoon freshly ground pepper**
- **2 teaspoons olive oil**
- **1 pound boneless leg of lamb, trimmed and cut into ½-inch pieces**
- **1 onion, chopped**
- **3 garlic cloves, minced**
- **1 (10-ounce) package frozen peas and carrots**
- **¾ cup reduced-sodium beef broth**
- **1 tablespoon Dijon mustard**
- **1 teaspoon Worcestershire sauce**

1 Combine the potatoes and parsnip with enough cold water to cover by 3 inches in a large pot; bring to a boil. Cook until fork-tender, 10–12 minutes; drain. Return the potatoes and parsnip to the pot. Add the milk, butter, ½ teaspoon of the salt, and ⅛ teaspoon of the pepper; mash with a potato masher or wooden spoon until smooth. Set aside.

2 Meanwhile, preheat the oven to 350°F. Spray a 1½-quart baking dish with nonstick spray.

3 To make the filling, heat the oil in a large nonstick skillet over medium-high heat. Add the lamb and cook, stirring occasionally, until browned, 3–4 minutes. Transfer to a plate. Add the onion and garlic to the same skillet; cook, stirring occasionally, until the onion begins to soften, about 2 minutes. Add the peas and carrots; cook, stirring occasionally, until thawed, 2–3 minutes. Add the lamb and cook, stirring occasionally, until heated through, 2–3 minutes. Stir in the broth, mustard, Worcestershire sauce, and the remaining ½ teaspoon salt and ⅛ teaspoon pepper; bring to a boil. Cook until sauce thickens slightly, 1–2 minutes.

4 Transfer the filling to the baking dish. Spread the potato mixture over the filling; smooth with a spatula. Bake until potato topping is crisp and the filling is bubbly around the edges, 25–30 minutes. Let cool 5 minutes before serving.

PER SERVING (about 1 cup): 279 Cal, 8 g Fat, 3 g Sat Fat, 0 g Trans Fat, 49 mg Chol, 606 mg Sod, 34 g Carb, 5 g Fib, 19 g Prot, 72 mg Calc. ***POINTS*** value: ***5.***

EXPRESS LANE Skip step 1 and substitute 4 cups cooked instant mashed potatoes for the fresh potato-parsnip mixture.

Cumin- and Fennel-Crusted Lamb Chops

HANDS-ON PREP **5 MIN**
COOK **6 MIN**
SERVES **4**

- **1 teaspoon cumin seeds, lightly crushed**
- **½ teaspoon fennel seeds, lightly crushed**
- **½ teaspoon dried oregano**
- **½ teaspoon salt**
- **¼ teaspoon freshly ground pepper**
- **4 (¼-pound) bone-in rib lamb chops, 1 inch thick, trimmed**

1 Spray the broiler rack with olive oil nonstick spray; preheat the broiler.

2 Combine the cumin seeds, fennel seeds, oregano, salt, and pepper in a cup. Press the spice mixture onto both sides of the lamb; place on the broiler rack. Broil the lamb 5 inches from the heat until an instant-read thermometer inserted in the side of each chop registers 145°F for medium, 3–4 minutes on each side.

PER SERVING (1 lamb chop): 107 Cal, 5 g Fat, 2 g Sat Fat, 0 g Trans Fat, 45 mg Chol, 332 mg Sod, 1 g Carb, 0 g Fib, 15 g Prot, 21 mg Calc. ***POINTS*** value: ***3.***

GOOD IDEA Keep a box of unflavored regular or whole-wheat couscous in your pantry of **Core Plan** ingredients to serve with speedy dishes like this (2/3 cup cooked couscous for each serving will increase the ***POINTS*** value by 2).

CUMIN- AND FENNEL-
CRUSTED LAMB CHOPS

CHAPTER SEVEN

SIMPLY

SEAFOOD

HONEY TERIYAKI SALMON

Honey Teriyaki Salmon

HANDS-ON PREP **5 MIN**
COOK **10 MIN**
SERVES **4**

- **¼ cup reduced-sodium soy sauce**
- **1 tablespoon chopped peeled fresh ginger**
- **1 tablespoon honey**
- **1 tablespoon fresh lemon juice**
- **1 garlic clove, crushed**
- **4 (¼-pound) skinless salmon fillets**

1 Whisk together the soy sauce, ginger, honey, lemon juice, and garlic in a small bowl until the honey has dissolved; pour into a large zip-close plastic bag. Add the salmon, squeeze out the air, and seal the bag; turn to coat the salmon. Refrigerate, turning the bag occasionally, at least 6 hours or up to 24 hours.

2 Remove the salmon from the marinade; transfer the remaining marinade to a small bowl.

3 Spray a large ridged grill pan or nonstick skillet with nonstick spray and set over medium heat. Add the salmon and cook 5 minutes. Turn the salmon, brush with the reserved marinade (discard any excess marinade), and cook until just opaque in the center, about 5 minutes more. Serve at once.

PER SERVING (1 fillet): 173 Cal, 4 g Fat, 1 g Sat Fat, 0 g Trans Fat, 65 mg Chol, 689 mg Sod, 6 g Carb, 0 g Fib, 26 g Prot, 17 mg Calc. ***POINTS*** value: ***4.***

GOOD IDEA This marinated salmon is also delicious chilled. Make 1½ times the marinade and add 2 extra salmon fillets to the recipe. Prepare as directed then wrap and refrigerate the extra cooked fillets up to 2 days. That way you'll have chilled salmon to make another meal later in the week. Serve with a favorite rice pilaf dish if desired.

Salmon with Mustard and Caraway

HANDS-ON PREP **5 MIN**
COOK **15 MIN**
SERVES **4**

- **4 teaspoons maple syrup**
- **2 tablespoons Dijon mustard**
- **4 (¼-pound) skinless salmon fillets**
- **1 tablespoon caraway seeds**

1 Preheat the oven to 400°F. Spray a large baking dish with nonstick spray.
2 Spread the maple syrup, then the mustard on the salmon. Sprinkle with the caraway seeds.
3 Arrange the salmon, mustard-side up, in the baking dish. Bake until just opaque in the center, about 15 minutes.

PER SERVING (1 fillet): 170 Cal, 5 g Fat, 1 g Sat Fat, 0 g Trans Fat, 65 mg Chol, 147 mg Sod, 6 g Carb, 1 g Fib, 25 g Prot, 35 mg Calc. ***POINTS*** value: ***4.***

GOOD IDEA This flavorful fish dish is perfect with a side of mashed potatoes (½ cup cooked potatoes for each serving will increase the ***POINTS*** value by 2).

Cold Poached Salmon with Horseradish Sauce

HANDS-ON PREP **10 MIN**
COOK **15 MIN**
SERVES **6**

- **1 large onion, sliced thinly into rings**
- **1 teaspoon allspice berries, crushed**
- **½ teaspoon whole cloves**
- **1 bay leaf**
- **1 (1½-pound) salmon fillet**
- **4 cups reduced-sodium vegetable broth**
- **½ cup + 2 tablespoons plain fat-free Greek-style yogurt**
- **1 tablespoon prepared grated horseradish in vinegar, drained**
- **1 tablespoon minced red onion**
- **½ teaspoon salt**

1 Place the onion rings in the bottom of a large pot or Dutch oven. Sprinkle the allspice and cloves among the onions; tuck in the bay leaf. Place the salmon, skin-side down, on top of the onion mixture, then pour the broth all around the fish.

2 Bring the broth to a simmer over medium heat. Reduce the heat and cook, covered, until the salmon is just opaque in the center, about 10 minutes. Uncover and remove the pot from the heat. Let the salmon cool in the broth 20 minutes.

3 With a spatula, carefully transfer the salmon to a cutting board; peel off the skin. Transfer the salmon to a serving platter, cover with plastic wrap, and refrigerate until chilled, at least 1 hour or up to 24 hours.

4 Meanwhile, whisk together the yogurt, horseradish, red onion, and salt in a small bowl. Cover and refrigerate until the flavors are blended, at least 1 hour or up to 24 hours. Serve with the salmon.

PER SERVING (⅙ of salmon with 2 tablespoons sauce): 166 Cal, 4 g Fat, 1 g Sat Fat, 0 g Trans Fat, 66 mg Chol, 366 mg Sod, 4 g Carb, 0 g Fib, 27 g Prot, 81 mg Calc. ***POINTS*** value: **4.**

TRY IT Greek-style yogurt, available in many large supermarkets, is extra thick and rich-tasting. If you can't find it, make yogurt cheese as a substitute: Spoon 1¼ cups plain fat-free yogurt into a coffee filter or cheesecloth-lined strainer and place over a bowl. Refrigerate, covered, until reduced by half, about 4 hours.

Tuna Burgers

HANDS-ON PREP **10 MIN**
COOK **10 MIN**
SERVES **4**

- **1 pound tuna steak, cut into 2-inch pieces**
- **3 tablespoons chopped fresh tarragon**
- **1 tablespoon Dijon mustard**
- **2 teaspoons Worcestershire sauce**
- **½ teaspoon freshly ground pepper**

1 Put the tuna in a food processor and pulse until finely chopped. Transfer to a large bowl; stir in the tarragon, mustard, Worcestershire sauce, and pepper. Shape into 4 patties.
2 Spray a large ridged grill pan or nonstick skillet with canola nonstick spray and set over medium heat. Add the patties and cook until browned and done to taste, about 4 minutes on each side for medium. Serve at once.

PER SERVING (1 burger): 128 Cal, 1 g Fat, 0 g Sat Fat, 0 g Trans Fat, 49 mg Chol, 163 mg Sod, 1 g Carb, 0 g Fib, 26 g Prot, 35 mg Calc. ***POINTS*** value: ***3.***

GOOD IDEA Double this recipe and keep the extra uncooked patties, individually wrapped, in the freezer up to 2 months. No need to bother with thawing—just cook the patties straight from the freezer 5 to 6 minutes on each side for a quick bite when you need it.

Bass with Warm Vinaigrette Dressing

HANDS-ON PREP **5 MIN**
COOK **15 MIN**
SERVES **4**

1 teaspoon cumin seeds
4 (¼-pound) bass fillets
1 medium shallot, minced
1 tablespoon rice vinegar
¾ cup reduced-sodium vegetable broth
¼ teaspoon salt

1 Place the cumin seeds in a large nonstick skillet over medium-low heat. Cook, stirring occasionally, until fragrant, about 2 minutes. Transfer to a small bowl.
2 Spray the same skillet with canola nonstick spray and set over medium-high heat. Add the fillets, skin-side down, and cook, shaking the pan constantly the first 30 seconds to prevent sticking, until crispy, about 5 minutes. Turn the fillets and cook until just opaque in the center, about 1 minute. Transfer the fillets skin-side up to a serving platter.
3 To make the dressing, heat the same skillet over medium-high heat. Add the shallot and cook, stirring constantly, until softened, about 1 minute. Add the vinegar and boil until reduced to a glaze, about 10 seconds. Add the broth and bring to a simmer, stirring to scrape up any browned bits from the bottom of the skillet. Cook the sauce until reduced by half; stir in the salt. Pour the sauce over the fillets, sprinkle with the cumin seeds and serve at once.

PER SERVING (1 fillet with 1½ tablespoons sauce and ¼ teaspoon cumin seeds): 124 Cal, 3 g Fat, 1 g Sat Fat, 0 g Trans Fat, 49 mg Chol, 327 mg Sod, 2 g Carb, 0 g Fib, 22 g Prot, 23 mg Calc. ***POINTS*** value: ***3.***

FOOD NOTE Use lake, fresh-water, or large-mouth bass, or striped, spotted, or black sea bass. Avoid using Chilean sea bass, a white-flesh fish which is not really bass and suffers from over-fishing.

Tuna with Caramelized Onions

HANDS-ON PREP **15 MIN**
COOK **35 MIN**
SERVES **4**

- **1 tablespoon olive oil**
- **3 onions, thinly sliced**
- **1 yellow bell pepper, seeded and cut into long thin strips**
- **4 (¼-pound) tuna steaks, ½-inch thick**
- **¼ teaspoon salt**
- **Pinch freshly ground pepper**
- **¼ cup dry white wine or water**
- **¼ cup chopped fresh parsley**

1 Heat the oil in a large nonstick skillet over medium heat. Add the onions and cook, stirring occasionally, until translucent, about 10 minutes. Add the bell pepper and cook, stirring occasionally, until the onions are browned and very soft, about 20 minutes. Transfer the onion mixture to a medium bowl; set aside.

2 Sprinkle the tuna with the salt and ground pepper. Heat the same skillet over medium-high heat. Add the tuna and cook until lightly browned, about 3 minutes. Turn the tuna and top each steak with one-quarter of the onion mixture. Add the wine and parsley and cook, covered, until the tuna is pink in the center, 2–3 minutes. Serve at once.

PER SERVING (1 tuna steak with ½ cup onion mixture and 2 tablespoons sauce): 191 Cal, 5 g Fat, 1 g Sat Fat, 0 g Trans Fat, 49 mg Chol, 191 mg Sod, 10 g Carb, 2 g Fib, 27 g Prot, 44 mg Calc. ***POINTS*** value: ***4.***

HOW WE DID IT For best results, caramelize the onion mixture in a heavy nonstick skillet. If the mixture starts to stick before the onions are browned, add a tablespoon or so of water.

TUNA WITH CARAMELIZED ONIONS

Herb-Stuffed Striped Bass

HANDS-ON PREP **10 MIN**

COOK **40 MIN**

SERVES **4**

- **2 (1½-pound) whole striped bass or red snapper, cleaned, tails and heads on (optional)**
- **¼ teaspoon salt**
- **⅛ teaspoon freshly ground pepper**
- **1 cup coarse fresh bread crumbs**
- **1 small red onion, finely chopped**
- **¼ cup finely chopped fresh cilantro or parsley**
- **2 teaspoons olive oil**
- **1 cup dry white wine or water**

1 Preheat the oven to 400°F. Spray a 9 x 13-inch baking dish with olive oil nonstick spray. Sprinkle half the salt and pepper inside the fish cavities.

2 To make the stuffing, combine the bread crumbs, red onion, cilantro, and the remaining salt and pepper in a medium bowl. Place half the stuffing inside each fish cavity and fasten each cavity closed with toothpicks.

3 Transfer the fish to the baking dish; drizzle with the oil. Pour the wine into the dish; cover tightly with foil. Bake until the fish are just opaque in the center, about 40 minutes. Remove the toothpicks and skin before eating. Serve at once with the stuffing.

PER SERVING (½ fish with about ⅓ cup stuffing): 339 Cal, 9 g Fat, 2 g Sat Fat, 0 g Trans Fat, 169 mg Chol, 524 mg Sod, 21 g Carb, 1 g Fib, 41 g Prot, 96 mg Calc. ***POINTS*** value: ***7.***

GOOD IDEA Serve the fish with steamed red potatoes to help soak up all the savory pan juices (1 cup cooked potatoes for each serving will increase the ***POINTS*** value by 2).

Spicy Red Snapper

HANDS-ON PREP **10 MIN**
COOK **25 MIN**
SERVES **6**

3 tablespoons fresh lime juice

2 teaspoons Red Spice Blend (see TIP below)

3 (½-pound) red snapper or pompano fillets, each cut crosswise in half

3 small firm-ripe bananas

½ cup coconut milk

1 Combine the lime juice and Red Spice Blend in a 9 x 13-inch baking dish. Add the fillets, turn to coat, and refrigerate, turning twice, 30 minutes.
2 Meanwhile, preheat the oven to 350°F. Cut each banana lengthwise in half then crosswise to make 12 pieces. Add the bananas and coconut milk to the baking dish; cover tightly with foil. Bake until the fillets are just opaque in the center, about 25 minutes. Serve at once.

PER SERVING (½ fillet with 2 banana pieces and 3 tablespoons sauce): 198 Cal, 6 g Fat, 4 g Sat Fat, 0 g Trans Fat, 40 mg Chol, 52 mg Sod, 14 g Carb, 2 g Fib, 23 g Prot, 45 mg Calc. ***POINTS*** value: ***4.***

HOW WE DID IT To make our fiery Red Spice Blend, combine 1 tablespoon whole black peppercorns, 1 tablespoon annatto seeds, ½ teaspoon cinnamon, ¼ teaspoon ground cumin, ⅛ teaspoon ground cloves, and ⅛ teaspoon ground allspice in a mini food processor or spice grinder and process to a fine powder. You'll only need half the amount for this recipe (it makes 4 teaspoons), but it also makes a great rub for chicken or pork.

STRIPED BASS WITH MUSHROOMS AND TANGERINE

Striped Bass with Mushrooms and Tangerine

HANDS-ON PREP **15 MIN**
COOK **25 MIN**
SERVES **4**

- **2** **(1½-pound) whole striped bass or red snapper, cleaned, tails and heads on (optional)**
- **2** **tablespoons fresh lemon juice**
- **¼** **teaspoon salt**
- **⅛** **teaspoon freshly ground pepper**
- **1** **tablespoon olive oil**
- **2** **cups sliced fresh button mushrooms**
- **2** **scallions, thinly sliced**
- **2** **tablespoons chopped fresh parsley**
- **1** **cup fresh tangerine juice**

1 Preheat the oven to 400°F. Spray a 9 x 13-inch baking dish with nonstick spray.

2 Sprinkle the fish and inside the fish cavities with the lemon juice, salt, and pepper. Transfer the fish to the baking dish; drizzle with the oil.

3 Combine the mushrooms, scallions, and parsley in a medium bowl; sprinkle over the fish. Pour the tangerine juice into the baking dish; cover tightly with foil. Bake until the fish are just opaque in the center, 25–30 minutes. Transfer the fish a serving platter. Top with the mushrooms and sauce. Remove the skin before eating.

PER SERVING (½ of fish with ½ cup mushrooms and sauce): 273 Cal, 9 g Fat, 2 g Sat Fat, 0 g Trans Fat, 169 mg Chol, 293 mg Sod, 9 g Carb, 1 g Fib, 39 g Prot, 50 mg Calc. ***POINTS*** value: ***6.***

GOOD IDEA Tangerines are at their sweetest and most plentiful in mid-winter, but if they aren't in season, this dish is equally delicious if you use fresh orange juice instead. You might like to stir a few fresh tangerine or orange sections into the mushroom mixture before serving with the fish.

Lemon-Pepper Snapper

HANDS-ON PREP **5 MIN**
COOK **10 MIN**
SERVES **4**

- **4** **(¼-pound) skinless red snapper fillets**
- **1** **tablespoon lemon-pepper seasoning**
- **2** **tablespoons fresh lemon juice**
- **¼** **cup reduced-sodium vegetable broth**
- **1** **tablespoon unsalted butter**

1 Sprinkle both sides of the fillets with the lemon-pepper seasoning.
2 Spray a large nonstick skillet with nonstick spray and set over medium-high heat. Add the fillets and cook until just opaque in the center, about 2½ minutes on each side. Transfer to a serving platter.
3 Add the lemon juice to the same skillet and cook, stirring to scrape up any browned bits from the bottom of the skillet. Stir in the broth and bring to a boil; boil 30 seconds. Whisk in the butter until melted. Pour the sauce over the fillets and serve at once.

PER SERVING (1 fillet with 1 tablespoon sauce): 139 Cal, 4 g Fat, 2 g Sat Fat, 0 g Trans Fat, 48 mg Chol, 410 mg Sod, 1 g Carb, 0 g Fib, 23 g Prot, 39 mg Calc. ***POINTS*** value: ***3.***

HOW WE DID IT When sautéing white-fleshed fish fillets like red snapper, cod, or grouper, add the fish to the hot skillet skin-side up (or gray-side up from which the skin has been removed). This way, when the fillets are turned once during cooking, they'll be presented with the more appealing white side facing up.

Flounder with Grapes and Almonds

HANDS-ON PREP **10 MIN**
COOK **10 MIN**
SERVES **4**

- **2** **tablespoons sliced almonds**
- **4** **(¼-pound) skinless flounder fillets**
- **¼** **teaspoon salt**
- **¼** **teaspoon freshly ground pepper**
- **1** **tablespoon olive oil**
- **1** **medium shallot, minced**
- **1** **cup green seedless grapes, halved**
- **2** **tablespoons white-wine vinegar**
- **1** **tablespoon chopped fresh thyme**

1 Place the almonds in a large nonstick skillet over medium-low heat. Cook, stirring occasionally, until golden and fragrant, about 4 minutes. Transfer to a small bowl.
2 Sprinkle the fillets with the salt and pepper. Spray the same skillet with nonstick spray and set over medium heat. Add the fillets and cook until lightly browned and just opaque in the center, about 2 minutes on each side. Transfer the fillets to a platter.
3 Heat the oil in the skillet over medium heat. Add the shallot and cook, stirring frequently, until softened, about 1 minute. Add the grapes and vinegar, stirring to scrape any browned bits from the bottom of the pan. Cook 30 seconds, then stir in the thyme and almonds. Spoon the sauce over the fillets and serve at once.

PER SERVING (1 fillet with ⅓ cup sauce): 174 Cal, 6 g Fat, 1 g Sat Fat, 0 g Trans Fat, 53 mg Chol, 230 mg Sod, 10 g Carb, 1 g Fib, 20 g Prot, 31 mg Calc. ***POINTS*** value: ***4.***

FOOD NOTE For a tasty nutrient boost, toast an extra bunch of almonds in step 1 and keep handy to stir into your favorite cereal or fat-free yogurt. Almonds are a great source of Vitamin E and Folic Acid (1 tablespoon sliced almonds per serving will increase the ***POINTS*** value by 1).

Swordfish Souvlaki Pitas

HANDS-ON PREP **15 MIN**
COOK **5 MIN**
SERVES **6**

- **1½** pounds skinless swordfish steaks, cut into 12 (½-inch-thick) strips
- **4** garlic cloves, minced
- **1** tablespoon fresh lemon juice
- **1** teaspoon dried oregano
- **1** teaspoon dried thyme
- **1** cup plain fat-free yogurt
- **1** medium cucumber, halved lengthwise, seeded, and chopped
- **1** tablespoon white-wine vinegar
- **½** teaspoon salt
- **½** teaspoon freshly ground pepper
- **3** cups shredded iceberg lettuce
- **2** cups diced tomatoes
- **6** (6-inch) whole-wheat pita breads, split

1 Gently combine the swordfish, half the garlic, the lemon juice, oregano, and thyme in a large bowl; cover and refrigerate, stirring occasionally, 20 minutes.
2 Meanwhile, combine the yogurt, cucumber, vinegar, salt, pepper, and the remaining garlic in a medium bowl and set aside.
3 Spray a large ridged grill pan or nonstick skillet with nonstick spray and set over medium heat. Add the swordfish and cook until just opaque in the center, about 2½ minutes on each side.
4 Spoon ½ cup of the lettuce, ⅓ cup of the tomatoes, ⅓ cup of the yogurt sauce, and 3 strips of the swordfish into each of the pita breads. Serve at once.

PER SERVING (1 sandwich): 347 Cal, 6 g Fat, 2 g Sat Fat, 0 g Trans Fat, 42 mg Chol, 668 mg Sod, 46 g Carb, 7 g Fib, 31 g Prot, 104 mg Calc. ***POINTS*** value: ***7.***

MAKE IT CORE Instead of making sandwiches, skip the pitas and serve the swordfish, lettuce, tomatoes, and yogurt sauce over whole-wheat couscous. This recipe would also work well with firm-fleshed tuna steak.

SWORDFISH SOUVLAKI PITAS

Curried Cod

HANDS-ON PREP **10 MIN**
COOK **20 MIN**
SERVES **4**

1 onion, finely chopped
1 medium apple, peeled and chopped
¼ cup raisins, chopped
1½ tablespoons curry powder
¾ cup long-grain white rice
2 cups reduced-sodium vegetable broth
1 (1-pound) skinless cod fillet, cut into 4 pieces

1 Spray a 2-quart nonstick saucepan or a small Dutch oven with nonstick spray and set over medium heat. Add the onion and cook, stirring frequently, until softened, about 3 minutes. Add the apple, raisins, and curry powder; cook, stirring constantly, until fragrant, about 30 seconds.
2 Stir in the rice and broth; bring to a boil. Reduce the heat, nestle the cod into the mixture, and simmer, covered, until the cod is just opaque in the center and the rice is tender, about 18 minutes. Serve at once.

PER SERVING (1 piece cod and ¾ cup rice mixture): 222 Cal, 1 g Fat, 0 g Sat Fat, 0 g Trans Fat, 43 mg Chol, 333 mg Sod, 32 g Carb, 3 g Fib, 20 g Prot, 49 mg Calc. ***POINTS*** value: ***4.***

FOOD NOTE Curry powder is simply a blend of spices—and no two brands are alike. If you're feeling adventurous, look for curry powder in East Indian markets or high-end food stores for a wider selection, including those based on cayenne, not the usual turmeric. In general, yellow curry powders are milder than their fiery, red kin.

Oven-Fried Catfish

HANDS-ON PREP **10 MIN**
COOK **15 MIN**
SERVES **4**

1 egg white
3 tablespoons water
¾ cup dried whole-wheat bread crumbs
1 teaspoon dried thyme
1 teaspoon ground cumin
1 teaspoon paprika
1 teaspoon celery seeds
1 teaspoon onion powder
½ teaspoon garlic powder
½ teaspoon salt
¼ teaspoon cayenne
4 (¼-pound) skinless catfish fillets

1 Preheat the oven to 400°F. Spray a large baking sheet with nonstick spray.
2 Whisk together the egg white and water until foamy in a shallow bowl. On a sheet of wax paper, combine the bread crumbs, thyme, cumin, paprika, celery seeds, onion powder, garlic powder, salt, and cayenne.
3 Dip the fillets in the egg white mixture, shaking off the excess, then in the bread crumb mixture, pressing gently to coat. Place on the baking sheet and lightly spray with nonstick spray. Bake until browned and just opaque in the center, about 12 minutes. Serve at once.

PER SERVING (1 fillet): 188 Cal, 10 g Fat, 2 g Sat Fat, 0 g Trans Fat, 51 mg Chol, 388 mg Sod, 8 g Carb, 1 g Fib, 20 g Prot, 27 mg Calc. ***POINTS*** value: ***4.***

GOOD IDEA Double the recipe for the whole-wheat bread crumb mixture and refrigerate in a zip-close plastic bag up to 1 week. They'll make an excellent coating for skinless boneless chicken breasts or another fish dinner.

HALIBUT PROVENÇAL

Halibut Provençal

HANDS-ON PREP **10 MIN**
COOK **35 MIN**
SERVES **4**

- **1 large onion, chopped**
- **1 fennel bulb, trimmed and chopped**
- **2 garlic cloves, minced**
- **8 plum tomatoes, chopped**
- **1 cup reduced-sodium vegetable broth**
- **1 tablespoon chopped fresh rosemary**
- **2 teaspoons chopped fresh thyme**
- **½ teaspoon salt**
- **¼ teaspoon freshly ground pepper**
- **4 (¼-pound) skinless halibut fillets**

1 Spray a large nonstick skillet with olive oil nonstick spray and set over medium heat. Add the onion and fennel; cook, stirring frequently, until softened, about 5 minutes. Add the garlic and cook, stirring constantly, just until fragrant, about 20 seconds. Add the tomatoes and cook, stirring frequently, until softened and the mixture is bubbly, about 4 minutes. Add the broth, rosemary, thyme, salt, and pepper; bring to a simmer, stirring to scrape up any browned bits from the bottom of the skillet.

2 Nestle the halibut into the sauce. Reduce the heat and simmer, covered, until the halibut is just opaque in the center, about 20 minutes. Serve at once.

PER SERVING (1 fillet with ¾ cup sauce): 167 Cal, 3 g Fat, 0 g Sat Fat, 0 g Trans Fat, 35 mg Chol, 508 mg Sod, 12 g Carb, 3 g Fib, 25 g Prot, 79 mg Calc. ***POINTS*** value: ***3.***

GOOD IDEA If plum or any other fresh tomato looks less than ripe for this recipe, just use a (28-ounce) can Italian tomatoes, drained and coarsely chopped, instead.

Spinach-Stuffed Trout

HANDS-ON PREP **15 MIN**
COOK **25 MIN**
SERVES **6**

- **1** (10-ounce) package frozen chopped spinach, thawed and squeezed dry
- **¾** cup crumbled reduced-fat feta cheese
- **2** tablespoons egg substitute
- **2** teaspoons chopped fresh dill, or 1 teaspoon dried
- **1** teaspoon onion powder
- **½** teaspoon garlic powder
- **¼** teaspoon ground nutmeg
- **¼** teaspoon salt
- **3** (¾-pound) whole trout, cleaned

1 Preheat the oven to 375°F.
2 To make the filling, put the spinach, cheese, egg substitute, dill, onion powder, garlic powder, nutmeg, and salt in a food processor; pulse until cheese is evenly distributed and the mixture is chunky.
3 Stuff the cavity of each trout with one-third of the filling. Transfer the trout to a 9 x 13-inch baking dish. Spray the trout with canola nonstick spray, turn over, and spray again. Bake until the filling is bubby and the trout is just opaque in the center, about 25 minutes. Serve at once.

PER SERVING (½ stuffed trout): 169 Cal, 8 g Fat, 2 g Sat Fat, 0 g Trans Fat, 54 mg Chol, 372 mg Sod, 3 g Carb, 2 g Fib, 22 g Prot, 117 mg Calc. ***POINTS*** value: ***4.***

MAKE IT CORE It's easy to enjoy this dish if you're following the **Core Plan,** just replace the reduced-fat feta with the fat-free variety of the cheese.

Asian Shrimp Packets

HANDS-ON PREP **15 MIN**
COOK **20 MIN**
SERVES **4**

1 pound medium shrimp, peeled and deveined

3 cups fresh snow peas, trimmed

2 cups bean sprouts

2 red bell peppers, seeded and thinly sliced

4 scallions, thinly sliced

4 garlic cloves, minced

2 tablespoons minced peeled fresh ginger

2 tablespoons reduced-sodium soy sauce

2 tablespoons rice vinegar

2 teaspoons hot chili paste

2 teaspoons Asian (dark) sesame oil

1 Preheat the oven to 400°F.

2 Combine all the ingredients in a large bowl.

3 Place 2 (16-inch) sheets of parchment paper on top of each other on a work surface. Spoon one-quarter of the shrimp mixture in the center of the paper. To make a packet, bring up the sides of the paper to meet in the center and fold over the edges, then fold the edges of the ends together. Allowing room for the packets to expand, crimp the edges. Place on a large baking sheet. Repeat with 6 more sheets of parchment paper and the remaining shrimp mixture to make a total of 4 packets.

4 Bake the packets until the shrimp are just opaque in the center, about 20 minutes. Let the packets stand on the baking sheet 10 minutes before serving. Open the packets carefully to let the steam excape. Serve at once, drizzled with any juices.

PER SERVING (1 packet): 176 Cal, 4 g Fat, 1 g Sat Fat, 0 g Trans Fat, 129 mg Chol, 502 mg Sod, 14 g Carb, 4 g Fib, 22 g Prot, 90 mg Calc. ***POINTS*** value: ***3.***

GOOD IDEA This spicy shrimp dish would be perfect paired with a bowl of nutritious and aromatic basmati brown rice to help tame the heat (1/2 cup cooked rice will increase the per-serving ***POINTS*** value by 2).

Grilled Shrimp with Mango Salsa

HANDS-ON PREP **20 MIN**
COOK **4 MIN**
SERVES **4**

1 lime

1 teaspoon grated orange zest

2 pounds large shrimp, in the shells

1 jalapeño pepper, seeded and chopped (wear gloves to prevent irritation)

1 tablespoon ancho chili powder or chili powder

3 garlic cloves, minced

1 teaspoon ground cumin

¼ teaspoon salt

Pinch cayenne

MANGO SALSA

2 large mangoes, peeled, pitted, and diced

1 small red onion, finely chopped

2 tablespoons finely chopped fresh cilantro

1 tablespoon fresh lime juice

Pinch salt

Pinch cayenne

1 Grate 1 teaspoon zest from the lime. Juice the lime. Combine the lime juice, lime and orange zests, and shrimp in a large bowl. Stir in the jalapeño, chili powder, garlic, cumin, salt, and cayenne. Cover and refrigerate the shrimp mixture 30 minutes.
2 Meanwhile, soak 4 (6–8-inch) wooden skewers in water at least 30 minutes.
3 To make the Mango Salsa, combine the mangoes, red onion, cilantro, lime juice, salt, and cayenne in a medium bowl.
4 Spray the grill rack with canola nonstick spray; prepare the grill for a medium-hot fire. Thread 4–5 shrimp on each of the skewers. Cover the ends of the skewers with foil to prevent them from charring. Place the skewers on the grill rack and grill about 4 inches from the heat until the shrimp are just opaque in the center, 1–2 minutes on each side. Serve at once with the salsa.

PER SERVING (1 skewer with ½ cup salsa): 248 Cal, 2 g Fat, 1 g Sat Fat, 0 g Trans Fat, 336 mg Chol, 574 mg Sod, 20 g Carb, 2 g Fib, 37 g Prot, 86 mg Calc. ***POINTS*** value: ***5.***

EXPRESS LANE Skip the Mango Salsa and serve the shrimp with your favorite prepared fat-free tomato salsa instead.

GRILLED SHRIMP WITH MANGO SALSA

Shrimp Satay

HANDS-ON PREP **30 MIN**
COOK **5 MIN**
SERVES **6**

- **1½ pounds large shrimp, peeled and deveined**
- **1 tablespoon curry powder**
- **¼ cup reduced-sodium soy sauce**
- **3 tablespoons natural peanut butter**
- **3 tablespoons rice vinegar**
- **1 garlic clove, crushed**
- **1 teaspoon sugar**
- **½ teaspoon ground ginger**
- **½ teaspoon freshly ground pepper**

1 Soak 12 (12-inch) wooden skewers in water at least 30 minutes. Meanwhile, combine the shrimp and curry powder in a large bowl; mix well.

2 To make the sauce, whisk together the soy sauce, peanut butter, vinegar, garlic, sugar, ginger, and pepper in a medium bowl until smooth; set aside.

3 Spray the broiler rack with nonstick spray and preheat the broiler.

4 Thread the shrimp onto the skewers. Cover the ends of the skewers with foil to prevent them from charring. Place the skewers on the broiler rack. Broil 5 inches from the heat until the shrimp are just opaque in the center, about 2½ minutes on each side. Serve at once with the sauce.

PER SERVING (2 skewers with 1½ tablespoons sauce): 150 Cal, 5 g Fat, 1 g Sat Fat, 0 g Trans Fat, 168 mg Chol, 627 mg Sod, 4 g Carb, 1 g Fib, 21 g Prot, 40 mg Calc. ***POINTS*** value: ***3.***

GOOD IDEA We prefer natural peanut butter (readily available in most supermarkets) for the dipping sauce, because it has less sugar and a nuttier taste than conventional brands.

Shrimp and Peppers

HANDS-ON PREP **15 MIN**
COOK **15 MIN**
SERVES **4**

- **1 large onion, thinly sliced**
- **2 red bell peppers, seeded and thinly sliced**
- **2 green bell peppers, seeded and thinly sliced**
- **6 garlic cloves, slivered**
- **2 plum tomatoes, chopped**
- **2 teaspoons chopped fresh oregano, or 1 teaspoon dried**
- **1 teaspoon fennel seeds**
- **½ teaspoon crushed red pepper**
- **1 pound medium shrimp, peeled and deveined**
- **4 teaspoons aged balsamic vinegar**

1 Spray a large nonstick skillet with olive oil nonstick spray and set over medium heat. Add the onion and bell peppers; cook, stirring frequently, until softened, about 4 minutes. Add the garlic and cook, stirring constantly, just until fragrant, about 30 seconds. Add the tomatoes, oregano, fennel seeds, and crushed red pepper; cook, stirring frequently, until the tomatoes soften, about 2 minutes.
2 Add the shrimp and cook, stirring frequently, until just opaque in the center, about 5 minutes. Divide the shrimp and peppers among 4 plates; drizzle each serving with 1 teaspoon of the vinegar and serve at once.

PER SERVING (1¼ cups): 149 Cal, 2 g Fat, 0 g Sat Fat, 0 g Trans Fat, 168 mg Chol, 202 mg Sod, 15 g Carb, 4 g Fib, 20 g Prot, 71 mg Calc. ***POINTS*** value: ***2.***

TRY IT This recipe is a great opportunity to use aged balsamic vinegar, a dark luscious condiment that gets its pungent sweetness from aging in wood barrels. While pricey, just a drizzle adds dramatic flavor not only to salads, but seafood dishes like this one as well as roasted meat and poultry.

SCALLOP, ORANGE, AND
ASPARAGUS STIR-FRY

Scallop, Orange, and Asparagus Stir-Fry

HANDS-ON PREP **20 MIN**
COOK **10 MIN**
SERVES **4**

- **2 large oranges**
- **2 tablespoons reduced-sodium soy sauce**
- **2 tablespoons reduced-sodium chicken broth**
- **1 tablespoon Worcestershire sauce**
- **1 tablespoon balsamic vinegar**
- **1½ pounds pencil-thin fresh asparagus, cut into 1-inch pieces**
- **4 large garlic cloves, slivered**
- **2 tablespoons minced peeled fresh ginger**
- **¼ teaspoon crushed red pepper**
- **1 pound sea scallops, each cut into 2 rounds**
- **1 small white potato, peeled and finely shredded**

1 With a vegetable peeler, remove wide strips of the zest from each orange and set aside. Cut off the rind, then section each orange over a bowl, allowing the sections to fall into the bowl. Stir in the soy sauce, broth, Worcestershire sauce, and vinegar.

2 Spray a large nonstick skillet or wok with canola nonstick spray and set over medium-high heat. Add the asparagus, garlic, ginger, and crushed red pepper; stir-fry until the asparagus are crisp-tender, about 2 minutes. Add the scallops and stir-fry until just opaque in the center, about 3 minutes. Add the orange mixture and reserved orange strips; bring to a boil, stirring constantly. Boil about 30 seconds. Add the potato and cook, stirring constantly, until the potato is tender and the mixture thickens, about 1 minute. Serve at once.

PER SERVING (1¼ cups): 205 Cal, 1 g Fat, 0 g Sat Fat, 0 g Trans Fat, 56 mg Chol, 646 mg Sod, 21 g Carb, 3 g Fib, 26 g Prot, 72 mg Calc. ***POINTS*** value: ***4.***

HOW WE DID IT Try this nifty technique for grating the potato in step 2: Hold a box grater over the skillet and grate the potato through the smallest holes right into the stir-fry.

Enlightened Lobster Rolls

HANDS-ON PREP **10 MIN**
COOK **5 MIN**
SERVES **4**

1 pound cooked fresh or frozen thawed shelled lobster meat, chopped
4 large romaine lettuce leaves, torn
1 celery stalk, minced
¼ cup fat-free mayonnaise
2 tablespoons fat-free sour cream
2 teaspoons fresh lemon juice
1½ teaspoons prepared horseradish, drained
1 teaspoon Worcestershire sauce
1 teaspoon ketchup
4 whole-wheat hot dog buns, split and toasted

1 Combine the lobster, lettuce, celery, mayonnaise, sour cream, lemon juice, horseradish, Worcestershire sauce, and ketchup in a bowl.
2 Spoon one-quarter of the lobster mixture into each bun to make 4 rolls.

PER SERVING (1 roll): 249 Cal, 3 g Fat, 1 g Sat Fat, 0 g Trans Fat, 83 mg Chol, 811 mg Sod, 28 g Carb, 4 g Fib, 27 g Prot, 122 mg Calc. ***POINTS*** value: ***4.***

GOOD IDEA Switch from the classic filling and substitute chopped cooked shrimp, scallops, or crabmeat for the lobster.

ENLIGHTENED LOBSTER ROLLS

Baked Crab Cakes

HANDS-ON PREP **20 MIN**
COOK **20 MIN**
SERVES **6**

- **3** celery stalks, minced
- **2** large shallots, minced
- **1** pound cooked fresh or thawed frozen lump crabmeat, picked over
- **¾** cup fat-free mayonnaise
- **1¾** cups dried whole-wheat bread crumbs
- **3** tablespoons minced fresh dill, or 1 tablespoon dried
- **2** tablespoons Dijon mustard
- **½** teaspoon salt
- **½** teaspoon freshly ground pepper
- **1–2** dashes hot pepper sauce

1 Preheat the oven to 400°F. Spray a large baking sheet with nonstick spray.
2 Spray a large nonstick skillet with nonstick spray and set over low heat. Add the celery and shallots; cook, stirring frequently, until golden and very soft, about 8 minutes. Transfer to a large bowl and let cool 10 minutes. Stir in the crab, mayonnaise, ¼ cup of the crumbs, the dill, mustard, salt, ground pepper, and pepper sauce; mix well. Shape the mixture by ⅓ cupfuls into 12 patties.
3 Spread the remaining 1½ cups crumbs on a large plate. Coat the patties evenly in the crumbs and transfer to the baking sheet. Lightly spray the cakes with nonstick spray. Bake until lightly browned and cooked through, about 12 minutes.

PER SERVING (2 cakes): 174 Cal, 7 g Fat, 1 g Sat Fat, 0 g Trans Fat, 74 mg Chol, 884 mg Sod, 13 g Carb, 2 g Fib, 16 g Prot, 108 mg Calc. ***POINTS*** value: ***4.***

GOOD IDEA For an elegant presentation, arrange 2 crab cakes on a bed of mesclun greens with a lemon wedge.

CHAPTER EIGHT

MEATLESS

MAIN DISHES

Southwestern Stuffed Peppers

HANDS-ON PREP **15 MIN**
COOK **1 HR**
SERVES **4**

- **4** green bell peppers
- **10** ounces reduced-fat firm tofu, cubed (about 2 cups)
- **2** cups cooked brown rice
- **¼** cup raisins, chopped
- **¼** cup shredded Monterey Jack cheese
- **¼** cup packed fresh cilantro leaves, chopped
- **2** tablespoons chopped red onion
- **2** tablespoons pine nuts
- **1** teaspoon ground cumin
- **½** teaspoon dried oregano
- **1** cup prepared mild salsa
- **1** cup water

1 Preheat the oven to 350°F. In a large pot of boiling water, cook the bell peppers until crisp-tender, about 2 minutes. Drain in a colander; rinse under cold running water. Drain; cut off the top of each bell pepper and remove the seeds.
2 To make the filling, combine the tofu, rice, raisins, cheese, cilantro, red onion, pine nuts, cumin, and oregano in a large bowl.
3 Stuff the filling evenly into each bell pepper. Place the stuffed peppers in a medium deep casserole or 1½-quart soufflé dish. Combine the salsa and water in a medium bowl; pour around the stuffed peppers. Cover with foil and bake, spooning the salsa mixture over the stuffed peppers once or twice, until the bell peppers are tender and the stuffing is heated through, about 45 minutes. Serve the bell peppers with the sauce.

PER SERVING (1 stuffed pepper with ¼ cup sauce): 282 Cal, 6 g Fat, 2 g Sat Fat, 0 g Trans Fat, 6 mg Chol, 570 mg Sod, 46 g Carb, 6 g Fib, 13 g Prot, 111 mg Calc. ***POINTS*** value: ***5.***

GOOD IDEA If you prefer your stuffed peppers even spicier, use hot salsa in the sauce—or substitute pepperjack for the Monterey Jack cheese.

Lentil Tofu Burgers

HANDS-ON PREP **10 MIN**
COOK **40 MIN**
SERVES **4**

- **1 cup lentils picked over, rinsed, and drained**
- **6 ounces firm tofu, cubed (about 1 cup)**
- **1 garlic clove, minced**
- **2 tablespoons fat-free egg substitute**
- **1 tablespoon rice vinegar**
- **1 teaspoon ground cumin**
- **1 teaspoon onion powder**
- **1 teaspoon salt**
- **¼ teaspoon ground cloves**

1 Bring a large pot of water to a boil. Add the lentils, reduce the heat, and cook until they are tender but still hold their shape, about 25 minutes. Drain.
2 Put the lentils and the remaining ingredients in a food processor and pulse until it forms a salsa-like, chunky puree. Shape the mixture into 6 (4-inch) patties.
3 Spray a large nonstick skillet with canola nonstick spray and set over medium heat. Add the patties and cook until browned and firm, about 3 minutes on each side.

PER SERVING (1 burger): 232 Cal, 4 g Fat, 1 g Sat Fat, 0 g Trans Fat, 0 mg Chol, 608 mg Sod, 31 g Carb, 12 g Fib, 20 g Prot, 328 mg Calc. ***POINTS*** value: ***4.***

TRY IT Rice vinegar, a mild vinegar made from fermented rice, is available in the Asian aisle of most supermarkets. If you're following the **Core Plan,** be sure not to confuse it with "seasoned rice vinegar" which is sweetened with sugar.

KOREAN LETTUCE WRAPS

Korean Lettuce Wraps

HANDS-ON PREP **10 MIN**
COOK **NONE**
SERVES **6**

- ¼ cup reduced-fat peanut butter
- ¼ cup fresh lime juice
- 3 tablespoons reduced-sodium soy sauce
- 1 teaspoon packed light brown sugar
- 1 teaspoon Asian chili paste
- 1 teaspoon Asian (dark) sesame oil
- 1 pound reduced-fat firm tofu, cut into ½-inch cubes
- 2 medium red bell peppers, seeded and thinly sliced
- 5 radishes, thinly sliced
- ¼ cup packed fresh cilantro leaves
- ¼ cup packed fresh mint leaves
- 12 large Boston or Bibb lettuce leaves

1 To make the sauce, whisk together the peanut butter, lime juice, soy sauce, brown sugar, chili paste, and sesame oil in a medium bowl until smooth.
2 To make the filling, combine the tofu, bell peppers, radishes, cilantro, and mint in a large bowl; gently toss.
3 Divide the filling evenly among the lettuce leaves; top each with 1 tablespoon of the sauce. Roll up and serve at once.

PER SERVING (2 wraps): 129 Cal, 6 g Fat, 1 g Sat Fat, 0 g Trans Fat, 0 mg Chol, 434 mg Sod, 11 g Carb, 2 g Fib, 9 g Prot, 51 mg Calc. ***POINTS*** value: ***3.***

GOOD IDEA Double or even triple the sauce as directed in step 1 and use it to drizzle over grilled meat and poultry or to serve as a dipping sauce for vegetables (2 teaspoons has a per-serving ***POINTS*** value of ½). The sauce can be refrigerated in an airtight container up to 1 week.

Vegetarian Stuffed Cabbage

HANDS-ON PREP **30 MIN**
COOK **1 HR 35 MIN**
SERVES **4**

- **8** large Savoy cabbage leaves
- **1** onion, minced
- **2** celery stalks, thinly sliced
- **4** garlic cloves, minced
- **½** pound frozen soy crumbles
- **1** cup cooked brown rice
- **¼** cup chopped raisins
- **½** teaspoon caraway seeds
- **½** teaspoon dried thyme
- **1½** cups reduced-sodium vegetable broth
- **1** cup tomato puree (no salt added)
- **2** tablespoons apple-cider vinegar
- **1** tablespoon packed light brown sugar
- **½** teaspoon salt

1 Preheat the oven to 400°F. Spray a 9-inch square baking dish with nonstick spray.

2 Meanwhile, bring a large pot of water to a boil. Add the cabbage and return to a boil. Cook until the cabbage is pliable, about 8 minutes. Drain in a colander. Rinse the cabbage under cold running water; drain and transfer to a cutting board. Trim the thick ribs from the base of the leaves and set aside.

3 To make the filling, spray a medium nonstick skillet with nonstick spray and set over medium heat. Add the onion and celery; cook, stirring frequently, until softened, about 4 minutes. Add the garlic and cook, stirring constantly, just until fragrant, about 30 seconds. Transfer the vegetables to a large bowl; stir in the soy crumbles, rice, raisins, caraway seeds, and thyme.

4 Place ¼ cup of the filling in the center of each cabbage leaf. Fold in the sides of each leaf over the filling and roll up. Put the rolls, seam-side down, in the baking dish.

5 Whisk together the broth, tomato puree, vinegar, brown sugar, and salt in a large bowl; pour over the rolls. Cover the baking dish with foil and bake until the cabbage is very soft and the sauce is bubbly, about 1 hour 15 minutes.

PER SERVING (2 rolls): 235 Cal, 1 g Fat, 0 g Sat Fat, 0 g Trans Fat, 0 mg Chol, 823 mg Sod, 44 g Carb, 8 g Fib, 15 g Prot, 116 mg Calc. ***POINTS*** value: ***4.***

TRY IT Soy protein crumbles, sometimes labeled "meatless ground burger," are available in your supermarket's frozen foods section. Keep a supply handy in your freezer to provide a healthy helping of protein and to use in place of ground beef dishes.

Weight Watchers Magazine

It's all about losing weight and keeping it off!

In every issue you'll get:

- Over 25 delicious recipes…
- Tips & Strategies to help you succeed…
- Ongoing motivation and support

LESS THAN $2 AN ISSUE!

IT'S LIKE GETTING THREE ISSUES FREE!

WeightWatchers®

SUBSCRIPTION CARD

YES, send me 1 year (6 issues) of Weight Watchers at the low rate of just $11.95. At less than $2.00 an issue, I'll save 50% off the cover price!

NAME (PLEASE PRINT)

ADDRESS APT.

CITY STATE ZIP

☐ **Payment enclosed.** ☐ **Bill me.** P701CB

To subscribe to Weight Watchers Magazine, complete and mail this card today!

NO POSTAGE
NECESSARY
IF MAILED
IN THE
UNITED STATES

BUSINESS REPLY MAIL

FIRST-CLASS MAIL PERMIT NO. 585 MARION OH

POSTAGE WILL BE PAID BY ADDRESSEE

WeightWatchers.

PO BOX 1969
MARION OH 43306-2069

Squash Soufflé

HANDS-ON PREP **10 MIN**
COOK **50 MIN**
SERVES **4**

- **¼ cup fat-free egg substitute**
- **1 tablespoon unsalted butter**
- **1½ tablespoons all-purpose flour**
- **1 cup fat-free milk**
- **½ teaspoon ground nutmeg**
- **½ teaspoon paprika**
- **½ teaspoon salt**
- **¼ teaspoon freshly ground pepper**
- **1 (12-ounce) package frozen squash puree, thawed**
- **2 tablespoons grated Parmesan cheese**
- **3 egg whites, at room temperature**

1 Preheat the oven to 375°F. Spray a 2-quart soufflé dish with nonstick spray.

2 Place the egg substitute in a medium bowl and set aside.

3 Melt the butter in a large saucepan over medium heat. Add the flour and cook, whisking constantly, until the mixture turns golden, about 1 minute. Gradually whisk in the milk and cook, whisking constantly, until thick and smooth. Whisk in the nutmeg, paprika, salt, and pepper.

4 Whisk a small amount of the milk mixture into the egg substitute, then whisk all the egg substitute mixture into the milk mixture. Remove the pan from the heat; whisk in the squash and cheese until blended.

5 With an electric mixer on high speed, beat the egg whites in a large bowl until stiff peaks form, about 3 minutes. Gently fold in one-half of the egg whites into the squash mixture with a rubber spatula. Fold in the remaining egg whites just until blended. Pour the mixture into the soufflé dish. Bake until puffed and cooked through, about 45 minutes. Serve at once.

PER SERVING (1 cup): 136 Cal, 4 g Fat, 2 g Sat Fat, 0 g Trans Fat, 11 mg Chol, 444 mg Sod, 18 g Carb, 1 g Fib, 9 g Prot, 144 mg Calc. ***POINTS*** value: ***3.***

Green Chile-and-Corn Frittata

HANDS-ON PREP **10 MIN**
COOK **15 MIN**
SERVES **4**

- **6 large eggs**
- **½ cup frozen corn kernels, thawed**
- **1 (4½-ounce) can chopped green chiles**
- **¼ cup fat-free milk**
- **1 tablespoon chopped fresh parsley**
- **2 teaspoons chopped fresh thyme**
- **¼ teaspoon freshly ground pepper**
- **3 dashes hot pepper sauce, or to taste**
- **8 cherry tomatoes, halved**
- **1 scallion, cut into 1-inch pieces**

1 Whisk together the eggs, corn, chiles, milk, parsley, thyme, ground pepper, and pepper sauce in a large bowl.
2 Spray a medium nonstick skillet with canola nonstick spray and set over medium heat. Add the egg mixture; top with the tomatoes, cut-side up, and the scallion. Cook, covered, until the eggs are set, about 15 minutes. Cut into 4 wedges.

PER SERVING (1 wedge): 145 Cal, 8 g Fat, 2 g Sat Fat, 0 g Trans Fat, 319 mg Chol, 109 mg Sod, 8 g Carb, 1 g Fib, 11 g Prot, 64 mg Calc. ***POINTS*** value: ***3.***

FOOD NOTE If you like the top of your frittata browned, preheat the broiler while the eggs cook. After the eggs are set, place the frittata in the skillet under the broiler and broil until lightly browned, about 20 seconds. Be sure to use a nonstick skillet with an ovenproof handle or wrap the handle in foil.

GREEN CHILE-AND-CORN FRITTATA

Creamy Vegetable Cobbler

HANDS-ON PREP **10 MIN**
COOK **35 MIN**
SERVES **6**

- **1** onion, chopped
- **1** garlic clove, minced
- **1½** cups fat-free milk
- **1** cup reduced-sodium vegetable broth
- **1** cup + 2 tablespoons all-purpose flour
- **1** (16-ounce) bag frozen mixed vegetables, thawed
- **1** teaspoon dried tarragon
- **1** teaspoon dried oregano
- **½** teaspoon salt
- **¼** teaspoon freshly ground pepper
- **⅓** cup cornmeal
- **2** teaspoons baking powder
- **1** teaspoon sugar
- **1** teaspoon paprika
- **¼** cup fat-free egg substitute
- **2** tablespoons canola oil

1 Preheat the oven to 350°F. Spray a 9-inch square baking dish with nonstick spray.

2 To make the filling, spray a large nonstick saucepan with nonstick spray and set over medium heat. Add the onion and cook, stirring frequently, until softened, about 3 minutes. Add the garlic and cook, stirring constantly, just until fragrant, about 20 seconds. Stir in 1 cup of the milk and the broth. Vigorously whisk in the 2 tablespoons flour until smooth and cook, whisking constantly, until the mixture thickens and bubbles, about 2 minutes. Stir in the mixed vegetables, tarragon, oregano, salt, and pepper. Pour into the baking dish.

3 To make the topping, combine the 1 cup flour, the cornmeal, baking powder, sugar, and paprika in a large bowl. Stir in the remaining ½ cup milk, the egg substitute, and oil until a sticky dough forms. Drop by heaping tablespoons over the filling in the baking dish.

4 Bake until the topping is lightly browned and the filling bubbles, about 25 minutes.

PER SERVING (1⅔ cups): 248 Cal, 6 g Fat, 1 g Sat Fat, 0 g Trans Fat, 1 mg Chol, 499 mg Sod, 41 g Carb, 5 g Fib, 9 g Prot, 146 mg Calc. ***POINTS*** value: ***5.***

GOOD IDEA Substitute any variety of frozen vegetables for the standard mixed vegetables we use in this recipe. If you like peas and green beans, use a 10-ounce package of each. Just avoid any brands that are seasoned or contain butter flavoring.

Baked Spinach and Cheese Dumplings

HANDS-ON PREP **15 MIN**
COOK **50 MIN**
SERVES **4**

- **1 (10-ounce) package frozen chopped spinach, thawed**
- **1 cup fat-free ricotta cheese**
- **½ cup grated Parmesan cheese**
- **6 tablespoons fat-free egg substitute**
- **6 tablespoons whole-wheat flour**
- **1 teaspoon dried oregano**
- **1 teaspoon salt**
- **½ teaspoon ground nutmeg**
- **½ teaspoon freshly ground pepper**
- **1 small onion, chopped**
- **2 garlic cloves, minced**
- **½ pound fresh mushrooms, thinly sliced**
- **3 plum tomatoes, chopped**
- **1 teaspoon dried basil**

1 Put the spinach, ricotta, Parmesan, egg substitute, whole-wheat flour, oregano, ½ teaspoon of the salt, and the nutmeg in a food processor and process until the mixture forms a paste. Transfer the mixture to a large bowl and refrigerate, covered, until thick enough to hold its shape, at least 1 hour or up to 8 hours.

2 Meanwhile, preheat the oven to 350°F. Bring a large pot of water to a boil. Drop the spinach mixture by 20 heaping tablespoonfuls into the water. Reduce the heat and simmer until the dumplings are slightly firm and cooked through, about 10 minutes. Transfer the dumplings with a slotted spoon to a 9-inch square baking dish and discard the water. Set the baking dish aside.

3 To make the sauce, spray a large nonstick saucepan with nonstick spray and set over medium heat. Add the onion and garlic; cook, stirring frequently, until the onion softens, about 3 minutes. Add the mushrooms and cook, stirring occasionally, until the mushrooms have released then reabsorbed their liquid, about 4 minutes. Stir in the tomatoes, basil, and the remaining ½ teaspoon salt; cook, stirring occasionally, until the tomatoes soften, about 5 minutes.

4 Pour the sauce over the dumplings and bake until the sauce is bubbly and the dumplings are heated through, about 20 minutes.

PER SERVING (5 dumplings with about ¼ cup sauce): 195 Cal, 4 g Fat, 2 g Sat Fat, 0 g Trans Fat, 18 mg Chol, 644 mg Sod, 23 g Carb, 5 g Fib, 17 g Prot, 354 mg Calc. ***POINTS*** value: ***3.***

EGGPLANT CHEESE ROLLS

Eggplant Cheese Rolls

HANDS-ON PREP **15 MIN**
COOK **45 MIN**
SERVES **6**

- **1** large eggplant, peeled and cut lengthwise into 12 (¼-inch-thick) slices
- **1** tablespoon salt
- **1** (15-ounce) container fat-free ricotta cheese
- **1** cup shredded part-skim mozzarella cheese
- **¼** cup fat-free egg substitute
- **¼** cup packed fresh basil leaves, finely chopped
- **½** teaspoon ground nutmeg
- **½** teaspoon freshly ground pepper
- **1½** cups prepared fat-free marinara sauce

1 Sprinkle both sides of the eggplant with the salt; place on a large baking sheet and let stand 30 minutes.

2 Meanwhile, preheat the oven to 350°F. Spray a 9 x 13-inch baking dish with nonstick spray.

3 Pat the salted eggplant dry with paper towels. Rinse and dry the baking sheet. Spray both sides of the eggplant with nonstick spray; place on the baking sheet. Bake until the eggplant softens, about 20 minutes. Let the eggplant cool on the baking sheet, about 15 minutes.

4 To make the filling, combine the ricotta, mozzarella, egg substitute, basil, nutmeg, and pepper in a large bowl. Spread ¼ cup of the filling over each eggplant slice and roll up. Place the rolls, seam-side down, in the baking dish.

5 Pour the marinara sauce over the rolls and bake until the rolls are heated through and the sauce is bubbly, about 25 minutes.

PER SERVING (2 rolls with ¼ cup sauce): 161 Cal, 3 g Fat, 2 g Sat Fat, 0 g Trans Fat, 23 mg Chol, 579 mg Sod, 17 g Carb, 3 g Fib, 14 g Prot, 276 mg Calc. ***POINTS*** value: ***3.***

ZAP IT Instead of baking the rolls in step 5, speed up the cooking time by using the microwave. Place the rolls in a shallow microwavable dish. Cover with plastic wrap, then prick a few holes in the plastic. Microwave on High 5 minutes. Uncover and microwave until heated through and bubbly, 3 to 4 minutes.

Tex-Mex Mushroom Ragoût

HANDS-ON PREP **10 MIN**
COOK **25 MIN**
SERVES **2**

- **1 onion, chopped**
- **1 garlic clove, minced**
- **½ pound fresh cremini or white button mushrooms, quartered**
- **½ pound fresh portobello mushrooms, stems removed and diced**
- **1 (15-ounce) can pinto beans, rinsed and drained**
- **1 (4½-ounce) can chopped green chiles**
- **1 tablespoon ground cumin**
- **1 teaspoon dried oregano**
- **1 teaspoon dried thyme**
- **¼ teaspoon cinnamon**
- **¼ teaspoon salt**
- **¼ teaspoon freshly ground pepper**
- **4 teaspoons fresh lime juice**

1 Spray a large nonstick saucepan with canola nonstick spray and set over medium heat. Add the onion and cook, stirring frequently, until softened, about 1 minute. Add the garlic and cook, stirring constantly, just until fragrant, about 20 seconds. Add the cremini and portobello mushrooms; cook, stirring occasionally, until the mushrooms have released then reabsorbed their liquid, about 5 minutes.

2 Stir in the beans, chiles, cumin, oregano, thyme, cinnamon, salt, and pepper; bring to a simmer. Reduce the heat and cook until the ragoût is thickened, about 15 minutes. Ladle into 2 bowls; sprinkle each serving with 2 teaspoons of the lime juice.

PER SERVING (2½ cups): 250 Cal, 2 g Fat, 0 g Sat Fat, 0 g Trans Fat, 0 mg Chol, 971 mg Sod, 44 g Carb, 15 g Fib, 14 g Prot, 218 mg Calc. ***POINTS*** value: ***4.***

FOOD NOTE French *ragoût* (ra-GOO) is a stew traditionally prepared with meat, fish, or poultry. Our vegetarian version is just as thick and rich-tasting as the classic. However, if this stew thickens too much, stir in ½ cup water and simmer at least 2 minutes more to blend the flavors.

One-Pot Cabbage, Potatoes, and Beans

HANDS-ON PREP **15 MIN**
COOK **50 MIN**
SERVES **4**

- **1 tablespoon olive oil**
- **1 large onion, chopped**
- **8 cups shredded cabbage**
- **1½ teaspoons dried thyme**
- **½ teaspoon caraway seeds**
- **½ teaspoon salt**
- **½ teaspoon freshly ground pepper**
- **1 (15-ounce) can white beans, rinsed and drained**
- **1 pound white potatoes, peeled and cut into ½-inch pieces**
- **½ cup water**

1 Heat the oil in a large nonstick saucepan over medium heat. Add the onion and cook, stirring frequently, until softened, about 3 minutes. Add the cabbage and cook, stirring frequently, until wilted, about 4 minutes.

2 Add the thyme, caraway seeds, salt, and pepper; cook, stirring constantly, just until fragrant, about 30 seconds. Stir in the beans, potatoes, and water; bring to a simmer. Reduce the heat and cook, covered, stirring occasionally, until the potatoes are tender, about 40 minutes.

PER SERVING (1½ cups): 224 Cal, 4 g Fat, 1 g Sat Fat, 0 g Trans Fat, 0 mg Chol, 411 mg Sod, 42 g Carb, 8 g Fib, 7 g Prot, 113 mg Calc. ***POINTS*** value: ***4.***

EXPRESS LANE Save time by purchasing preshredded cabbage. You'll find it in the produce aisle of the supermarket. Or buy a small, 1½-pound cabbage and prep it with the shredding blade of a food processor.

Stuffed Portobello Mushrooms

HANDS-ON PREP **20 MIN**
COOK **25 MIN**
SERVES **2**

- **6 (4-inch) fresh portobello mushrooms**
- **1 small onion, chopped**
- **2 garlic cloves, minced**
- **1 (15-ounce) can black beans, rinsed and drained**
- **1 serrano pepper, seeded and thinly sliced (wear gloves to prevent irritation)**
- **2 teaspoons dried marjoram**
- **2 teaspoons Worcestershire sauce**
- **1 teaspoon dried oregano**
- **¼ teaspoon salt**
- **¼ teaspoon freshly ground pepper**
- **½ cup frozen corn kernels, thawed**

1 Preheat the oven to 400°F. Remove the stems from the mushrooms and coarsely chop; set aside. Place the mushroom caps, stem-side up, on a jelly-roll pan.

2 To make the filling, spray a large nonstick skillet with canola nonstick spray and set over medium heat. Add the onion and cook, stirring frequently, until softened, about 1 minute. Add the garlic and cook, stirring constantly, just until fragrant, about 20 seconds. Add the chopped mushrooms and cook, stirring occasionally, until softened, about 2 minutes. Transfer the mixture to a large bowl. Stir in the beans, serrano, marjoram, Worcestershire sauce, oregano, salt, and ground pepper. Transfer half the mushroom mixture to a food processor and process until smooth, then stir back into the remaining mushroom mixture. Stir in the corn.

3 Stuff the filling into each mushroom cap, mounding it in the center. Cover loosely with foil and bake 15 minutes. Uncover and bake until the mushrooms are browned and sizzling, about 5 minutes.

PER SERVING (3 stuffed mushrooms): 289 Cal, 2 g Fat, 0 g Sat Fat, 0 g Trans Fat, 0 mg Chol, 809 mg Sod, 50 g Carb, 15 g Fib, 18 g Prot, 113 mg Calc. ***POINTS*** value: ***5.***

FOOD NOTE Look for portobello mushrooms with firm, dry gills—not soft or slippery. The gills should also be fairly tight, rather than fanned wide open—a sure indicator that they're past their prime.

STUFFED PORTOBELLO MUSHROOMS

SUCCOTASH-STUFFED
ACORN SQUASH

Succotash-Stuffed Acorn Squash

HANDS-ON PREP **15 MIN**
COOK **1 HR**
SERVES **4**

- **2** **acorn squash, halved through the stem and seeded**
- **1½** **cups frozen lima beans, thawed**
- **1½** **cups frozen corn kernels, thawed**
- **1** **celery stalk, thinly sliced**
- **1** **plum tomato, chopped**
- **1** **small shallot, minced**
- **2** **tablespoons chili powder**
- **2** **teaspoons fresh lime juice**
- **½** **teaspoon salt**
- **¼** **teaspoon mustard powder**

1 Preheat the oven to 350°F. Spray a large jelly-roll pan with canola nonstick spray. Place the squash, cut-side down, on the pan. Bake until tender, about 40 minutes. Let cool 10 minutes.

2 Meanwhile, to make the filling, combine the remaining ingredients in a large bowl.

3 Transfer the squash, cut-side up, to a large baking dish. Stuff the filling into each squash half, mounding it in the center. Bake until heated through, about 20 minutes.

PER SERVING (1 stuffed squash half): 233 Cal, 2 g Fat, 0 g Sat Fat, 0 g Trans Fat, 0 mg Chol, 373 mg Sod, 53 g Carb, 14 g Fib, 9 g Prot, 105 mg Calc. ***POINTS*** value: ***4.***

GOOD IDEA It's easy to get a head start on this dish for a busy weeknight dinner. Prepare the recipe as directed through step 2, then cover and refrigerate the squash and filling separately up to 2 days. When ready to serve, stuff the squash and bake until heated through, about 30 minutes.

Spaghetti Squash with Broccoli Rabe and Beans

HANDS-ON PREP **15 MIN**
COOK **1 HR 10 MIN**
SERVES **4**

- **1** (3-pound) spaghetti squash, pricked several times with a fork
- **1** tablespoon olive oil
- **6** garlic cloves, slivered
- **1** (15-ounce) can white beans, rinsed and drained
- **¾** pound broccoli rabe, trimmed and chopped
- **½** teaspoon ground nutmeg
- **½** teaspoon crushed red pepper
- **½** teaspoon salt
- **½** teaspoon freshly ground pepper
- **½** cup vegetable broth
- **¼** cup grated Parmesan cheese

1 Preheat the oven to 350°F. Place the squash on a jelly-roll pan and roast until tender, about 1 hour. Let the squash stand on the pan until cool enough to handle, about 15 minutes.

2 Cut the squash in half lengthwise and scoop out the seeds. With a fork, scrape out the pulp and set aside.

3 Heat the oil in a large nonstick skillet over medium heat. Add the garlic and cook, stirring frequently, until softened, about 1 minute. Add the beans and broccoli rabe; cook, stirring constantly, until the broccoli rabe wilts, about 1 minute. Stir in the nutmeg, crushed red pepper, salt, and ground pepper. Add the broth, scraping up any browned bits from the bottom of the skillet with a spoon. Reduce the heat and simmer, covered, stirring occasionally, until the broccoli rabe is tender, about 5 minutes.

4 Add the reserved squash and cook, stirring occasionally, until heated through, about 2 minutes. Serve, sprinkled with the cheese.

PER SERVING (2 cups with 1 tablespoon cheese): 223 Cal, 6 g Fat, 2 g Sat Fat, 0 g Trans Fat, 4 mg Chol, 674 mg Sod, 35 g Carb, 7 g Fib, 10 g Prot, 202 mg Calc. ***POINTS*** value: ***4.***

FOOD NOTE Spaghetti squash is so named because once cooked, its sweet-tasting pulp separates into spaghetti-like strands. Choose a firm-fleshed, oval squash without any green spots—a sign the squash had been picked before it was ripe.

Curried Cauliflower and Chickpeas

HANDS-ON PREP **15 MIN**
COOK **25 MIN**
SERVES **4**

- **1** large onion, chopped
- **1** tablespoon minced peeled fresh ginger
- **2** garlic cloves, minced
- **2** tablespoons curry powder
- **6** cups cauliflower florets
- **1½** cups canned chickpeas, rinsed and drained
- **1** Golden Delicious apple, peeled and chopped
- **2** cups vegetable broth
- **½** cup plain Greek-style yogurt

1 Spray a large nonstick saucepan with nonstick spray and set over medium heat. Add the onion and cook, stirring frequently, until softened, about 3 minutes. Add the ginger and garlic; cook, stirring constantly, just until fragrant, about 30 seconds. Add the curry powder and cook, stirring constantly, just until fragrant, about 20 seconds. Add the cauliflower, chickpeas, and apple; cook, stirring constantly, until lightly browned, about 2 minutes.

2 Stir in the broth and bring to a simmer, scraping up any browned bits with a spoon. Reduce the heat and cook, covered, until the cauliflower is tender, about 15 minutes.

3 Remove the pan from the heat. Add the yogurt and stir until blended. Let the curry stand, covered, until the yogurt is heated through, about 5 minutes.

PER SERVING (about 2 cups): 211 Cal, 4 g Fat, 2 g Sat Fat, 0 g Trans Fat, 4 mg Chol, 656 mg Sod, 36 g Carb, 10 g Fib, 18 g Prot, 192 mg Calc. ***POINTS*** value: **4.**

MAKE IT CORE Switch the Greek-style yogurt with plain fat-free yogurt and enjoy this dish on the **Core Plan.**

Risotto with Peas

HANDS-ON PREP **15 MIN**
COOK **35 MIN**
SERVES **4**

- **2 teaspoons olive oil**
- **4 medium shallots, thinly sliced**
- **1 cup Arborio rice**
- **½ teaspoon freshly ground pepper**
- **¼ teaspoon salt**
- **¼ teaspoon saffron**
- **4 cups reduced-sodium vegetable broth**
- **2 cups hulled fresh peas or frozen peas, thawed**
- **¼ cup grated Parmesan cheese**
- **2 teaspoons Dijon mustard**

1 Heat the oil in a large nonstick saucepan over medium heat. Add the shallots and cook, stirring frequently, until softened, about 3 minutes. Add the rice, pepper, salt, and saffron; cook, stirring to coat, about 1 minute.

2 Add ¼ cup of the broth. Reduce the heat and cook, stirring frequently, until the liquid has been absorbed. Continue to add the broth, ¼ cup at a time, stirring until it is absorbed before adding more, until rice is just tender. The cooking time, from the first addition of broth, should be 25–30 minutes.

3 Stir in the peas, cheese, and mustard. Cook, stirring constantly, until the flavors are blended, about 3 minutes.

PER SERVING (1 cup): 269 Cal, 4 g Fat, 1 g Sat Fat, 0 g Trans Fat, 4 mg Chol, 904 mg Sod, 47 g Carb, 6 g Fib, 9 g Prot, 121 mg Calc. ***POINTS*** value: ***5.***

HOW WE DID IT The key to this creamy, yet low-fat, risotto is cooking the rice at the barest simmer over low heat. If the mixture simmers more quickly than 2 or 3 bubbles at a time, reduce the heat even further.

Vegetable Fried Rice

HANDS-ON PREP **15 MIN**
COOK **10 MIN**
SERVES **4**

- **¾ cup fat-free egg substitute**
- **6 scallions, cut into 1-inch pieces**
- **2 garlic cloves, minced**
- **2 tablespoons minced peeled fresh ginger**
- **1 (16-ounce) bag frozen mixed vegetables, thawed**
- **4 cups cooked brown rice**
- **½ cup vegetable broth**
- **¼ cup rice vinegar**
- **3 tablespoons reduced-sodium soy sauce**
- **1 teaspoon Asian (dark) sesame oil**
- **2 dashes hot pepper sauce, or to taste**

1 Spray a large nonstick skillet with nonstick spray and set over medium heat. Add the egg substitute and swirl to cover the pan. Cook, stirring gently, until set, about 1 minute. Transfer to a small bowl and set aside.

2 Spray the same skillet with nonstick spray and set over medium-high heat. Add the scallions, garlic, and ginger; stir-fry until the scallions soften, about 2 minutes. Add the mixed vegetables and stir-fry until crisp-tender, about 1 minute. Add the rice and stir-fry until blended and evenly coated, about 1 minute. Add the broth, vinegar, and soy sauce; cook, stirring constantly, until the liquid boils and is thoroughly incorporated into the rice, about 1 minute. Remove the skillet from the heat; stir in the reserved egg substitute, the sesame oil, and pepper sauce.

PER SERVING (1½ cups): 342 Cal, 4 g Fat, 1 g Sat Fat, 0 g Trans Fat, 0 mg Chol, 741 mg Sod, 64 g Carb, 9 g Fib, 15 g Prot, 80 mg Calc. ***POINTS*** value: ***6.***

GOOD IDEA Cook a generous supply of brown rice to have on hand for quick stir-fries like this, or to add fiber to soups and stews. Refrigerate in an airtight container up to 5 days.

GRILLED VEGETABLES AND COUSCOUS

Grilled Vegetables and Couscous

HANDS-ON PREP **10 MIN**
COOK **15 MIN**
SERVES **4**

- **2** large red onions, cut into ½-inch-thick rings
- **2** zucchini, each cut into 6 pieces
- **2** red bell peppers, seeded and each cut into 6 pieces
- **12** fresh pencil-thin asparagus spears, trimmed
- **1** eggplant, halved lengthwise and cut into ½-inch-thick slices
- **1½** cups reduced-sodium vegetable broth
- **1** cup couscous
- **½** cup walnut pieces, toasted and chopped
- **½** teaspoon dried oregano
- **½** teaspoon salt
- **½** teaspoon freshly ground pepper
- **3** tablespoons aged balsamic vinegar

1 Spray the grill rack with nonstick spray; prepare the grill for a medium-hot fire.
2 Place the vegetables, in batches if necessary, on the grill rack. Grill 5 inches from the heat, turning occasionally, until tender and evenly charred, about 8 minutes. Transfer each batch of vegetables to a plate.
3 Meanwhile, bring the broth to a boil in a small saucepan. Stir in the couscous, walnuts, oregano, salt, and pepper. Remove the saucepan from the heat; cover and let stand 5 minutes.
4 Fluff the couscous with a fork and divide among 4 plates. Top each serving with one-quarter of the vegetables; drizzle with the vinegar.

PER SERVING (1¾ cups couscous with about 2 cups vegetables and about 2 teaspoons vinegar): 365 Cal, 11 g Fat, 1 g Sat Fat, 0 g Trans Fat, 0 mg Chol, 510 mg Sod, 59 g Carb, 10 g Fib, 13 g Prot, 88 mg Calc. ***POINTS*** value: ***7.***

MAKE IT CORE Omit the walnuts if you're following the **Core Plan,** and sprinkle the dish with ½ cup crumbled fat-free feta cheese before drizzling with the vinegar in step 4.

Vegetable and Goat Cheese Terrine

HANDS-ON PREP **20 MIN**
COOK **30 MIN**
SERVES **8**

- **1 pound eggplant, peeled and cut lengthwise into 1/4-inch-thick slices**
- **3 medium zucchini, cut lengthwise into ¼-inch-thick slices**
- **2 yellow squash, cut lengthwise into ¼-inch-thick slices**
- **1 tablespoon salt**
- **12 fresh asparagus spears, trimmed**
- **½ pound goat cheese**
- **2 tablespoons packed fresh tarragon leaves, chopped**
- **½ teaspoon freshly ground pepper**
- **4 jarred roasted red bell peppers (not in oil)**
- **½ cup fat-free mayonnaise**
- **2 teaspoons Dijon mustard**
- **2 teaspoons Asian (dark) sesame oil**

1 Sprinkle both sides of the eggplant, zucchini, and squash with the salt; place on a large baking sheet and let stand 30 minutes.
2 Pat the salted vegetables dry with paper towels. Spray a large ridged grill pan with nonstick spray and set over medium heat. Add the vegetables, in batches, and cook until lightly charred and softened, 3–4 minutes on each side. Transfer each batch to a large plate. Add the asparagus to the pan and cook until crisp-tender, about 3 minutes on each side. Add to the vegetables.
3 Combine the cheese, tarragon, and ground pepper in a small bowl.
4 Line a 5 x 9-inch loaf pan with enough plastic wrap to hang over the sides of the pan by about 3 inches. Layer the bottom with half the eggplant, then half the zucchini, squash, and asparagus. Add 2 of the bell peppers, then spread the cheese mixture over the top. Layer the remaining asparagus, then the remaining squash, zucchini, and eggplant over the cheese. Cover the terrine with the plastic; weight down the top with 2 large heavy cans. Set the pan in a larger baking pan (to catch any drips) and refrigerate until firm, at least 12 hours or up to 3 days.
5 To make the sauce, puree the remaining 2 bell peppers, the mayonnaise, mustard, and sesame oil in a food processor. Cover and refrigerate in an airtight container until the flavors are blended, at least 12 hours or up to 3 days.
6 To serve, remove the cans, uncover the plastic, and invert the loaf pan onto a plate. Wipe the pan with hot, damp paper towels, then gently remove the pan. Remove the plastic; cut the terrine into 8 slices and serve with the sauce.

PER SERVING (1 slice with 1 generous tablespoon sauce): 172 Cal, 11 g Fat, 6 g Sat Fat, 0 g Trans Fat, 24 mg Chol, 465 mg Sod, 13 g Carb, 4 g Fib, 9 g Prot, 124 mg Calc. ***POINTS*** value: ***4.***

Cheesy Potato Gratin

HANDS-ON PREP **15 MIN**
COOK **1 HR 20 MIN**
SERVES **2**

- **1** onion, chopped
- **2** garlic cloves, minced
- **1** (4½-ounce) can chopped green chiles
- **1** teaspoon ground cumin
- **½** teaspoon freshly ground pepper
- **¼** teaspoon salt
- **3** dashes hot pepper sauce, or to taste
- **2** large baking potatoes, peeled and sliced paper thin
- **1** (10-ounce) package frozen chopped spinach, thawed and squeezed dry
- **¼** cup shredded reduced-fat cheddar cheese
- **⅔** cup reduced-sodium vegetable broth

1 Preheat the oven to 375°F. Spray an 8-inch square baking dish with nonstick spray.

2 Spray a large nonstick skillet with nonstick spray and set over medium heat. Add the onion and cook, stirring occasionally, until softened, about 3 minutes. Add the garlic and cook, stirring constantly, just until fragrant, about 20 seconds. Add the chiles, cumin, ground pepper, salt, and pepper sauce; cook, stirring constantly, until fragrant, about 30 seconds.

3 Spread half the potatoes in the baking dish. Layer the top with half the onion mixture, then the spinach and cheese. Top with the remaining potatoes and onion mixture. Gently press down the potatoes with the back of a spoon; pour the broth over the top.

4 Cover with foil and bake 1 hour. Uncover and bake until the gratin is lightly browned, about 15 minutes.

PER SERVING (2 cups): 290 Cal, 4 g Fat, 2 g Sat Fat, 0 g Trans Fat, 10 mg Chol, 929 mg Sod, 56 g Carb, 10 g Fib, 12 g Prot, 393 mg Calc. ***POINTS*** value: ***5.***

MAKE IT CORE It's easy to adjust this recipe to fit the **Core Plan**—just use fat-free instead of reduced-fat cheddar cheese.

CHAPTER NINE

ON THE

SIDE

Drunken Beans

HANDS-ON PREP **10 MIN**
COOK **1 HR 40 MIN**
SERVES **10**

- **1 (16-ounce) package dried pinto beans, picked over, rinsed, and drained**
- **1 tablespoon canola oil**
- **1 large white onion, chopped**
- **2 jalapeño peppers, seeded and finely chopped (wear gloves to prevent irritation)**
- **2 large garlic cloves, finely chopped**
- **1 bay leaf**
- **2 teaspoons dried oregano**
- **1 (48-ounce) can reduced-sodium chicken broth**
- **1 (12-ounce) bottle dark Mexican beer**
- **1 (6-ounce) smoked ham hock**
- **¾ teaspoon salt**

1 Presoak the beans according to package directions; drain.
2 Preheat the oven to 300°F. Heat the oil in a Dutch oven over medium-high heat. Add the onion and cook, stirring occasionally, until lightly browned, about 8 minutes. Add the jalapeño, garlic, bay leaf, and oregano; cook, stirring constantly, until fragrant, about 30 seconds. Stir in the beans, broth, beer, and ham hock; bring to a boil.
3 Transfer the Dutch oven to the oven and bake until the beans are tender, about 1½ hours. Discard the ham hock and bay leaf; stir in the salt.

PER SERVING (1 cup): 222 Cal, 5 g Fat, 1 g Sat Fat, 0 g Trans Fat, 15 mg Chol, 548 mg Sod, 30 g Carb, 10 g Fib, 15 g Prot, 63 mg Calc. ***POINTS*** value: ***4.***

FOOD NOTE These beans should remain whole and tender and swim in a generous amount of broth making them the perfect accompaniment to rice (½ cup cooked rice for each serving will increase the ***POINTS*** value by 2). If you prefer your beans less brothy, serve with a slotted spoon.

Wild Rice Pilaf with Cranberries and Pecans

HANDS-ON PREP **5 MIN**
COOK **1 HR 5 MIN**
SERVES **6**

- **3 cups reduced-sodium chicken broth**
- **1 cup wild rice, rinsed**
- **1 bunch scallions, chopped**
- **½ cup dried cranberries**
- **¼ cup fresh parsley leaves, chopped**
- **¼ cup coarsely chopped pecans**

1 Bring the broth to a boil in a medium saucepan; stir in the rice. Reduce the heat and simmer, covered, 20 minutes.
2 Stir in the scallions and cranberries; simmer, covered, until the grains start to pop and the rice is tender, 35–40 minutes. Fluff the rice with a fork; stir in the parsley and pecans.

PER SERVING (2/3 cup): 195 Cal, 6 g Fat, 1 g Sat Fat, 0 g Trans Fat, 3 mg Chol, 508 mg Sod, 33 g Carb, 3 g, Fib, 6 g Prot, 22 mg Calc. ***POINTS*** value: ***4.***

TRY IT Although its name suggests otherwise, wild rice isn't rice at all; it's a long-grain marsh grass native to the Great Lakes region of North America. While a bit expensive, wild rice is prized for its nutty flavor and chewy texture. Be sure to clean wild rice thoroughly before cooking it. Combine the rice and enough cold water to cover in a bowl and let stand a few minutes. Pour off the water and any debris that floats to the surface, then rinse again.

Tuscan Beans with Sage and Pancetta

HANDS-ON PREP **5 MIN**
COOK **15 MIN**
SERVES **6**

- **1 teaspoon olive oil**
- **2 garlic cloves, minced**
- **2 ounces thinly sliced pancetta, cut into strips**
- **2 (15-ounce) cans cannellini or Great Northern beans, drained (do not rinse)**
- **¼ cup fresh sage leaves, chopped**
- **½ teaspoon salt**
- **Freshly ground pepper, to taste**

1 Heat the oil in a medium saucepan over medium heat. Add the garlic and cook, stirring frequently, just until fragrant, about 1 minute. Add the pancetta and cook, stirring occasionally, until crisp, about 3 minutes.

2 Add the beans and sage; cook, stirring occasionally, until the flavors are blended, about 10 minutes. Stir in the salt and pepper.

PER SERVING (¾ cup): 116 Cal, 4 g Fat, 1 g Sat Fat, 0 g Trans Fat, 8 mg Chol, 486 mg Sod, 14 g Carb, 4 g Fib, 5 g Prot, 39 mg Calc. ***POINTS*** value: ***2.***

GOOD IDEA Serve this classic Italian side with simple pan-seared pork chops. A 3-ounce bone-in chop, cooked, for each serving will increase the ***POINTS*** value by 4.

TUSCAN BEANS WITH SAGE
AND PANCETTA

MEXICAN-STYLE RED RICE

Mexican-Style Red Rice

HANDS-ON PREP **15 MIN**
COOK **35 MIN**
SERVES **8**

- **1 tablespoon canola oil**
- **1 onion, chopped**
- **1 cup long-grain white rice**
- **2 garlic cloves, chopped**
- **1½ teaspoons chili powder**
- **1 (14½-ounce) can reduced-sodium chicken broth**
- **½ cup water**
- **2 carrots, diced**
- **½ teaspoon salt**
- **1 (14½-ounce) can diced tomatoes with jalapeños, drained**
- **⅓ cup frozen corn kernels**
- **⅓ cup frozen peas**

1 Heat the oil in a large saucepan over medium-high heat. Add the onion and cook, stirring occasionally, until softened, about 3 minutes. Add the rice and cook, stirring occasionally, until golden, 3–4 minutes. Add the garlic and chili powder; cook, stirring frequently, until fragrant, about 30 seconds.

2 Stir in the broth, water, carrots, and salt. Reduce the heat and simmer, covered, 15 minutes. Stir in the tomatoes, corn, and peas; return to a simmer. Cook, covered, until the rice is tender and the liquid is absorbed, about 10 minutes. Fluff with a fork before serving.

PER SERVING (¾ cup): 148 Cal, 2 g Fat, 0 g Sat Fat, 0 g Trans Fat, 0 mg Chol, 517 mg Sod, 28 g Carb, 2 g Fib, 4 g Prot, 33 mg Calc. ***POINTS*** value: ***3.***

GOOD IDEA If you prefer this traditional veggie-studded rice less spicy, reduce the chili powder to 1 teaspoon and use a can of regular diced tomatoes.

Hearty Stuffed Peppers

HANDS-ON PREP **10 MIN**
COOK **55 MIN**
SERVES **4**

2 (3½-ounce) packages boil-in-the-bag brown rice

4 large red bell peppers

1 teaspoon olive oil

1 medium white onion

1 garlic clove, finely chopped

¼ cup grated Parmesan cheese

1 tablespoon chopped fresh oregano

1 Preheat the oven to 350°F. Spray a medium baking dish with nonstick spray.
2 Cook the rice according to package directions omitting the salt, if desired.
3 Meanwhile, cut the stems and top ½ inch off the bell peppers and scoop out the seeds; set aside.
4 Heat the oil in a large nonstick skillet over medium-high heat. Add the white onion and garlic; cook until the onion softens, 2–3 minutes. Stir in the rice, cheese, and oregano. Stuff the filling into each bell pepper. Place the stuffed peppers in the baking dish. Bake until the peppers are tender and the filling is heated through, about 40 minutes.

PER SERVING (1 stuffed pepper): 273 Cal, 5 g Fat, 1 g Sat Fat, 0 g Trans Fat, 4 mg Chol, 108 mg Sod, 50 g Carb, 5 g Fib, 8 g Prot, 96 mg Calc. ***POINTS*** value: ***5.***

GOOD IDEA You can substitute 2 cups cooked quinoa or couscous for the cooked rice if you like and omit step 2.

Quinoa with Wild Mushrooms

HANDS-ON PREP **15 MIN**
COOK **25 MIN**
SERVES **6**

- **1** ounce dried porcini mushrooms
- **2** cups warm water
- **1** tablespoon olive oil
- **2** cups fresh white button mushrooms, sliced
- **2** garlic cloves, chopped
- **1** small shallot, minced
- **1** teaspoon chopped fresh oregano
- **1** cup quinoa
- **1** cup chicken broth
- **¼** cup dry white wine

1 Combine the porcini mushrooms and warm water in a medium bowl; cover and let soak about 30 minutes. With a slotted spoon, lift the mushrooms from the liquid, rinse thoroughly, and coarsely chop. Line a strainer with a paper towel. Pour the mushroom liquid through the strainer; reserve ¾ cup of the liquid.
2 Heat the oil in a medium saucepan over medium heat. Add the porcini mushrooms, white mushrooms, garlic, shallot, and oregano; cook, stirring occasionally, until the mushrooms are tender, about 5 minutes. Stir in the quinoa, broth, the reserved mushroom liquid, and the wine; bring to a boil. Reduce the heat and simmer, covered, until all the liquid is absorbed, 15–20 minutes. Fluff with a fork before serving.

PER SERVING (⅔ cup): 160 Cal, 5 g Fat, 1 g Sat Fat, 0 g Trans Fat, 1 mg Chol, 176 mg Sod, 24 g Carb, 3 g Fib, 6 g Prot, 24 mg Calc. ***POINTS*** value: ***3.***

TRY IT *Quinoa* (KEEN-wah), an ancient grain with a pleasantly mild flavor and slightly crunchy texture, is a nutrition powerhouse. Because it contains all eight essential amino acids, it is considered a complete protein. Look for quinoa at the supermarket or your local natural-foods store.

Citrus Beets

HANDS-ON PREP **15 MIN**
COOK **30 MIN**
SERVES **4**

- **1** **bunch fresh beets (about 5)**
- **1** **orange, peeled and cut into sections**
- **¼** **cup toasted and skinned hazelnuts, chopped**
- **3** **tablespoons white vinegar**
- **½** **teaspoon grated orange zest**
- **2** **tablespoons orange juice**
- **1** **tablespoon olive oil**
- **½** **teaspoon salt**
- **Freshly ground pepper, to taste**

1 Preheat the oven to 450°F. Arrange the beets on a baking sheet; roast until fork-tender, about 30 minutes. Let cool. Peel and cut into cubes. Transfer the beets to a medium bowl; add the orange and hazelnuts.
2 Meanwhile, whisk together the vinegar, orange zest, orange juice, oil, salt, and pepper in a small bowl. Drizzle the dressing over the salad; toss to coat.

PER SERVING (about ½ cup): 119 Cal, 8 g Fat, 1 g Sat Fat, 0 g Trans Fat, 0 mg Chol, 339 mg Sod, 12 g Carb, 3 g Fib, 3 g Prot, 33 mg Calc. ***POINTS*** value: ***2.***

FOOD NOTE This is a delightful salad to serve chilled with grilled poultry like our Grilled Chicken with Salsas (page 126). Just refrigerate in an airtight container up to 3 days.

CITRUS BEETS

SWISS CHARD WITH TOMATOES

Swiss Chard with Tomatoes

HANDS-ON PREP **15 MIN**
COOK **30 MIN**
SERVES **6**

- **2 pounds Swiss chard, tough stems discarded, leaves coarsely chopped**
- **1 tablespoon canola oil**
- **1 onion, finely chopped**
- **2 garlic cloves, finely chopped**
- **1 jalapeño pepper, seeded and minced (wear gloves to prevent irritation)**
- **3 tomatoes, seeded and coarsely chopped**
- **½ teaspoon salt**
- **1 teaspoon grated lemon zest**

1 Bring a Dutch oven of lightly salted water to a boil. Add the chard and cook until bright green, about 1 minute. Drain.
2 Heat the oil in the same Dutch oven over medium-high heat. Add the onion and cook, stirring occasionally, until softened, about 3 minutes. Add the garlic and jalapeño; cook, stirring frequently, until fragrant, about 30 seconds. Add the tomatoes and cook, stirring occasionally, until softened, about 3 minutes. Add the chard and salt; cook, covered, stirring occasionally, until the chard is tender, 6–8 minutes. Stir in the lemon zest and serve at once.

PER SERVING (2/3 cup): 78 Cal, 3 g Fat, 0 g Sat Fat, 0 g Trans Fat, 0 mg Chol, 444 mg Sod, 12 g Carb, 4 g Fib, 4 g Prot, 98 mg Calc. ***POINTS*** value: ***1.***

FOOD NOTE Like Swiss chard, other dark leafy greens, such as kale, dandelion greens, and broccoli rabe, are rich in vitamins and minerals and can be used in this zesty side dish. Or you can make this with an equal amount of fresh spinach. Just skip step 1 and add the spinach to the skillet in batches in step 2, stirring until each batch wilts and the spinach is tender, about 3 minutes.

Sautéed Spinach with Almonds and Grapes

HANDS-ON PREP **10 MIN**
COOK **10 MIN**
SERVES **4**

- **1 tablespoon extra-virgin olive oil**
- **1 onion, finely chopped**
- **2 tablespoons blanched sliced almonds**
- **2 garlic cloves, minced**
- **2 (10-ounce) bags triple-washed spinach leaves**
- **1 tablespoon water**
- **¼ teaspoon salt**
- **¼ teaspoon freshly ground pepper**
- **1 cup seedless red grapes, halved**

1 Heat the oil in a large nonstick skillet over medium-high heat. Add the onion and almonds; cook, stirring occasionally, until the onion is softened and the almonds are golden, about 5 minutes. Add the garlic and cook, stirring frequently, until fragrant, about 30 seconds.

2 Increase the heat to high. Add the spinach, in batches, the water, salt, and pepper, stirring just until each batch wilts. Add the grapes and cook, stirring occasionally, until heated through, about 2 minutes. Serve at once.

PER SERVING (1 cup): 154 Cal, 5 g Fat, 1 g Sat Fat, 0 g Trans Fat, 0 mg Chol, 373 mg Sod, 27 g Carb, 8 g Fib, 5 g Prot, 124 mg Calc. ***POINTS*** value: ***3.***

MAKE IT CORE Skip the nuts if you're following the **Core Plan** (the ***POINTS*** value for each serving will decrease by ½).

SAUTÉED SPINACH WITH
ALMONDS AND GRAPES

Spiced Cauliflower with Garlic

HANDS-ON PREP **10 MIN**
COOK **20 MIN**
SERVES **6**

- **1 tablespoon canola oil**
- **1 onion, finely chopped**
- **3 garlic cloves, minced**
- **2 teaspoons ground cumin**
- **¾ teaspoon salt**
- **½ teaspoon turmeric**
- **⅛ teaspoon cayenne**
- **1 head cauliflower, cut into 1-inch florets**
- **1½ cups water**
- **2 teaspoons sherry vinegar**

1 Heat the oil a Dutch oven over medium-high heat. Add the onion and cook, stirring occasionally, until softened, 4–5 minutes. Add the garlic, cumin, salt, turmeric, and cayenne; cook, stirring frequently, until fragrant, about 30 seconds. Stir in the cauliflower until coated with the spice mixture. Stir in the water and bring to a boil. Reduce the heat and simmer, covered, stirring occasionally, until the cauliflower is tender, 8–10 minutes.

2 Transfer the cauliflower with a slotted spoon to a serving bowl. Simmer the cooking liquid, uncovered, until reduced to ½ cup, about 4 minutes. Stir in the vinegar and pour over the cauliflower. Serve at once or let cool and serve at room temperature.

PER SERVING (1 cup): 61 Cal, 3 g Fat, 0 g Sat Fat, 0 g Trans Fat, 0 mg Chol, 322 mg Sod, 8 g Carb, 3 g Fib, 2 g Prot, 35 mg Calc. ***POINTS*** value: ***1.***

GOOD IDEA This savory side would be an ideal accompaniment to Cumin- and Fennel-Crusted Lamb Chops (page 182) or Lemon-Pepper Snapper (page 198).

Garlicky Haricots Verts

HANDS-ON PREP **10 MIN**
COOK **10 MIN**
SERVES **4**

1 pound haricot verts, trimmed

1 tablespoon olive oil

2 garlic cloves, chopped

2 tablespoons grated pecorino Romano cheese

Freshly ground pepper, to taste

Put the haricots verts in a steamer basket; set in a saucepan over 1 inch of boiling water. Cover tightly and steam until crisp-tender, 3–4 minutes. Transfer the haricots verts to a medium bowl. Add the oil and garlic; mix well. Sprinkle with the cheese and pepper and serve at once.

Per serving (1 cup): 76 Cal, 4 g Fat, 1 g Sat Fat, 0 g Trans Fat, 1 mg Chol, 22 mg Sod, 9 g Carb, 4 g Fib, 3 g Prot, 64 mg Calc. ***POINTS*** value: ***1.***

TRY IT Ultra-thin and tender *haricots verts* (ah-ree-koh VEHR), or French green beans, make an elegant side dish. While they're more widely available in supermarkets today, simply substitute fresh green beans if you can't find them. You may need to steam them an extra minute or so.

Summertime Corn and Tomato Sauté

HANDS-ON PREP **15 MIN**
COOK **5 MIN**
SERVES **4**

- **1 tablespoon olive oil**
- **2 cups fresh corn kernels (from 4 ears)**
- **4 plum tomatoes, seeded and diced**
- **1 medium red onion, chopped**
- **¼ cup chopped fresh basil**
- **2 tablespoons white vinegar**
- **½ teaspoon salt**
- **Freshly ground pepper, to taste**

Heat the oil in a large nonstick skillet over medium heat. Add the corn, tomatoes, and red onion; cook, stirring frequently, until the onion is softened and the mixture is heated through, 5–6 minutes. Remove the skillet from the heat; stir in the basil, vinegar, salt, and pepper. Serve at once, at room temperature, or chilled.

PER SERVING (¾ cup): 135 Cal, 5 g Fat, 1 g Sat Fat, 0 g Trans Fat, 0 mg Chol, 310 mg Sod, 24 g Carb, 3 g Fib, 3 g Prot, 13 mg Calc. ***POINTS*** value: ***3.***

GOOD IDEA Double the recipe, refrigerate half in an airtight container up to 2 days, and served chilled with canned tuna or salmon for another meal.

SUMMERTIME CORN AND TOMATO SAUTÉ

Curried Celeriac Slaw

HANDS-ON PREP **10 MIN**
COOK **NONE**
SERVES **6**

- **½ cup fat-free sour cream**
- **2 tablespoons fresh lemon juice**
- **1 tablespoon honey**
- **2 teaspoons curry powder**
- **½ teaspoon salt**
- **1 large (1-pound) celeriac, peeled and cut into matchstick-thin strips**
- **2 tart apples, chopped**
- **¾ cup golden raisins**
- **2 scallions, chopped**
- **Freshly ground pepper, to taste**

1 To make the dressing, whisk together the sour cream, lemon juice, honey, curry powder, and salt in a small bowl.
2 Combine the celeriac, apples, raisins, and scallions in a medium bowl. Add the dressing and pepper; toss to combine. Serve at once or cover and refrigerate up to 2 days.

PER SERVING (1 cup): 153 Cal, 1 g Fat, 0 g Sat Fat, 0 g Trans Fat, 0 mg Chol, 302 mg Sod, 36 g Carb, 4 g Fib, 3 g Prot, 79 mg Calc. ***POINTS*** value: ***2.***

EXPRESS LANE Replace the celeriac with a 1-pound bag of coleslaw mix from the produce aisle at the supermarket.

Sesame Broccoli

HANDS-ON PREP **10 MIN**
COOK **10 MIN**
SERVES **4**

- **4** **cups fresh broccoli florets**
- **3** **tablespoons reduced-sodium soy sauce**
- **2** **teaspoons Asian (dark) sesame oil**
- **1** **tablespoon grated peeled fresh ginger**
- **1** **teaspoon packed brown sugar**
- **1** **tablespoon black sesame seeds**
- **1** **tablespoon white sesame seeds**

1 Put the broccoli in a steamer basket; set in a saucepan over 1 inch of boiling water. Cover tightly and steam until crisp-tender, 4–5 minutes. Transfer the broccoli to a medium bowl.
2 Meanwhile, to make the dressing, whisk together the soy sauce, sesame oil, ginger, and brown sugar in a small bowl.
3 Add the dressing to the broccoli; toss to coat. Sprinkle with the sesame seeds and serve at once.

PER SERVING (1 cup): 79 Cal, 5 g Fat, 1 g Sat Fat, 0 g Trans Fat, 0 mg Chol, 474 mg Sod, 6 g Carb, 3 g Fib, 4 g Prot, 40 mg Calc. ***POINTS*** value: ***1.***

ZAP IT Instead of steaming, combine the broccoli and ¼ cup water in a large microwavable bowl. Cover with plastic wrap, then prick a few holes in the plastic. Microwave on High until crisp-tender, 2 to 3 minutes. Drain.

LEMON-DILL FINGERLING POTATOES

Lemon-Dill Fingerling Potatoes

HANDS-ON PREP **10 MIN**
COOK **35 MIN**
SERVES **4**

- **1 pound fingerling potatoes, scrubbed and cut lengthwise in half**
- **⅓ cup fresh dill, chopped**
- **2 tablespoons fresh lemon juice**
- **4 teaspoons olive oil**
- **½ teaspoon salt**
- **Freshly ground pepper, to taste**

1 Preheat the oven to 400°F. Line a large baking sheet with foil.
2 Combine the potatoes, dill, lemon juice, and oil in a bowl; spread in a single layer on the baking sheet. Roast 20 minutes; turn the potatoes. Roast the potatoes until tender and golden brown, 15–20 minutes. Sprinkle with the salt and pepper.

PER SERVING (¾ cup): 115 Cal, 5 g Fat, 1 g Sat Fat, 0 g Trans Fat, 0 mg Chol, 295 mg Sod, 15 g Carb, 2 g Fib, 3 g Prot, 7 mg Calc. ***POINTS*** value: ***2.***

GOOD IDEA Combine the potatoes, dill, lemon juice, and oil in a large zip-close plastic bag. Squeeze out the air and seal the bag; turn to coat the potatoes. Refrigerate overnight, then proceed with the recipe as directed.

CHAPTER TEN

BAKED GOODS

AND DESSERTS

Rustic Dinner Rolls

HANDS-ON PREP **20 MIN**
COOK **20 MIN**
SERVES **12**

1⅓ cups warm water (105–115°F)
1 tablespoon sugar
1 teaspoon salt
1 package active dry yeast
3 cups unbleached all-purpose flour

1 Combine the water, sugar, and salt in a large bowl. Sprinkle in the yeast and let stand until foamy, about 5 minutes.

2 Stir in the flour with a spoon until the dough starts to gather around the spoon. Turn the dough onto a lightly floured surface; knead until the dough is smooth and elastic, about 10 minutes.

3 Spray a large bowl with nonstick spray; put the dough in the bowl. Cover the bowl lightly with plastic wrap and let the dough rise in a warm spot until it doubles in size, about 2 hours.

4 Punch down the dough. Sprinkle a work surface lightly with flour. Turn the dough onto the surface and knead about 2 minutes. Let rest about 5 minutes.

5 Spray a large baking sheet with nonstick spray. Divide the dough into 12 pieces. Shape each piece into a ball and cover lightly with plastic wrap. Working 1 ball at a time, with a floured rolling pin, roll into a 3 x 5-inch oval. Starting at one short end, fold one-third of the dough to the center and press firmly to flatten. Repeat at the opposite end. Pinch the seams and the ends to seal. Rolling the dough with the palms of your hands, shape into a 7-inch roll with slightly tapered ends. Place the roll on the baking sheet. Repeat with the remaining dough to make 12 rolls. Cover lightly with plastic wrap and let the rolls rise in a warm spot until they nearly double in size, 45–60 minutes.

6 Preheat the oven to 400°F. With a sharp knife, make a small slash down the center of each roll. Brush the rolls lightly with water. Bake until golden and they sound hollow when tapped, 18–22 minutes. Serve warm or cool completely on a rack.

PER SERVING (1 roll): 121 Cal, 1 g Fat, 0 g Sat Fat, 0 g Trans Fat, 0 mg Chol, 195 mg Sod, 25 g Carb, 1 g Fib, 4 g Prot, 5 mg Calc. ***POINTS*** value: ***2.***

Olive Bread

HANDS-ON PREP **20 MIN**
COOK **40 MIN**
SERVES **12**

- **1¼ cups warm water (105–115°F)**
- **1 tablespoon sugar**
- **1 package active dry yeast**
- **1 tablespoon extra-virgin olive oil**
- **3¼ cups all-purpose flour**
- **2 teaspoons dried oregano**
- **1½ teaspoons salt**
- **½ teaspoon dried thyme**
- **20 pitted kalamata olives, halved**

1 Combine the water and sugar in a large bowl. Sprinkle in the yeast and let stand until foamy, about 5 minutes.

2 Stir in the oil, 3 cups of the flour, the oregano, salt, and thyme with a spoon until the dough starts to gather around the spoon. Add the olives and knead until blended, 5–6 times. Turn the dough onto a lightly floured surface; knead in the remaining ¼ cup flour, 1 tablespoon at a time, until smooth and elastic, about 10 minutes.

3 Spray a large bowl with nonstick spray; place the dough in the bowl. Cover the bowl lightly with plastic wrap and let the dough rise in a warm spot until it doubles in size, about 1½ hours.

4 Lightly flour a large baking sheet. Punch down the dough. Turn the dough onto a lightly floured surface and knead about 10 times. Shape into a 6-inch circle and transfer to the baking sheet. Cover and let the dough rise until it doubles in size, about 30 minutes.

5 Meanwhile, preheat the oven to 400°F. With a sharp knife, cut a ½-inch-deep X over the surface of the loaf. Bake until golden brown and the loaf sounds hollow when tapped, 40–45 minutes. Serve warm or cool completely on a rack. Cut into 12 slices.

PER SERVING (1 slice): 157 Cal, 3 g Fat, 0 g Sat Fat, 0 g Trans Fat, 0 mg Chol, 394 mg Sod, 28 g Carb, 1 g Fib, 4 g Prot, 13 mg Calc. ***POINTS*** value: ***3.***

GOOD IDEA Planning a gathering and want to serve freshly baked bread? You can start this recipe a day ahead! Prepare the recipe as directed through step 3 except use cold water instead of warm, and refrigerate the dough overnight. (Chilling will retard the rising plus allow the bread to develop more flavor.) The next day, just complete the recipe as directed from step 4.

SEMOLINA FENNEL-RAISIN BREAD

Semolina Fennel-Raisin Bread

HANDS-ON PREP **15 MIN**
COOK **40 MIN**
SERVES **12**

- **½ cup golden raisins**
- **½ cup hot water**
- **1½ cups warm water (105–115°F)**
- **2 teaspoons sugar**
- **1 package active dry yeast**
- **1¾ cups all-purpose flour**
- **1 cup semolina flour**
- **½ cup cornmeal**
- **1½ teaspoons fennel seeds**
- **1 teaspoon salt**

1 Combine the raisins and hot water in a small bowl; let stand until softened, about 10 minutes. Drain.
2 Meanwhile, combine the warm water and sugar in a large bowl. Sprinkle in the yeast and let stand until foamy, about 5 minutes.
3 Stir in 1½ cups of the all-purpose flour, the semolina flour, cornmeal, fennel seeds, and salt with a spoon until the dough starts to gather around the spoon. Add the softened raisins and knead until blended, 5–6 times. Turn the dough onto a lightly floured surface and knead in the remaining ¼ cup all-purpose flour, 1 tablespoon at a time, until smooth and elastic, about 8 minutes.
4 Spray a large bowl with nonstick spray; place the dough in the bowl. Cover the bowl lightly with plastic wrap and let the dough rise in a warm spot until it doubles in size, about 1½ hours.
5 Lightly flour a large baking sheet. Punch down the dough. Turn the dough onto a lightly floured surface and knead about 10 times. Shape into a 10-inch loaf and transfer to the baking sheet. Cover and let the dough rise until it doubles in size, about 30 minutes.
6 Meanwhile, preheat the oven to 400°F. Bake until golden brown and the loaf sounds hollow when tapped, 40–45 minutes. Serve warm or cool on a rack. Cut into 12 slices.

PER SERVING (1 slice): 164 Cal, 1 g Fat, 0 g Sat Fat, 0 g Trans Fat, 0 mg Chol, 197 mg Sod, 35 g Carb, 2 g Fib, 5 g Prot, 12 mg Calc. ***POINTS*** value: ***3.***

TRY IT Semolina flour is a coarsely ground (high-gluten) wheat flour. It's primarily used to make bread and pizza dough. Look for it in larger supermarkets or Italian specialty stores.

Green Chile Corn Bread

HANDS-ON PREP **10 MIN**
COOK **20 MIN**
SERVES **12**

- **1** cup all-purpose flour
- **¾** cup yellow cornmeal
- **1** tablespoon sugar
- **1** teaspoon baking powder
- **1** teaspoon salt
- **1** teaspoon ground cumin
- **¼** teaspoon baking soda
- **1** cup fat-free buttermilk
- **2** large eggs, lightly beaten
- **1** (4½-ounce) can diced green chiles, drained
- **3** tablespoons unsalted butter, melted
- **½** cup shredded reduced-fat sharp cheddar cheese

1 Preheat the oven to 425°F. Spray an 8-inch square baking pan with nonstick spray.
2 Combine the flour, cornmeal, sugar, baking powder, salt, cumin, and baking soda in a medium bowl. Combine the buttermilk, eggs, chiles, and melted butter in another medium bowl. Add the buttermilk mixture to the flour mixture and stir just until blended. Gently stir in the cheese. With a rubber spatula, transfer the batter to the pan and spread evenly.
3 Bake until the edges are golden and have pulled away from the sides of the pan, 20–22 minutes. Let cool in the pan on a rack, 10 minutes. Cut into 12 squares and serve warm.

PER SERVING (1 square): 135 Cal, 5 g Fat, 3 g Sat Fat, 0 g Trans Fat, 47 mg Chol, 318 mg Sod, 18 g Carb, 1 g Fib, 5 g Prot, 74 mg Calc. ***POINTS*** value: ***3.***

GOOD IDEA Leftover corn bread? Just wrap it tightly in plastic wrap and store at room temperature overnight or freeze up to 3 months. Serve lightly toasted for a savory start to your day or for a light snack.

GREEN CHILE
CORN BREAD

Irish Soda Bread

HANDS-ON PREP **15 MIN**
COOK **45 MIN**
SERVES **12**

- **2 cups all-purpose flour**
- **3 tablespoons sugar**
- **1 teaspoon baking powder**
- **1 teaspoon salt**
- **½ teaspoon baking soda**
- **2 tablespoons cold unsalted butter, cut into small pieces**
- **½ cup dried currants**
- **1 teaspoon caraway seeds**
- **1 cup low-fat buttermilk**

1 Preheat the oven to 350°F. Spray a baking sheet with nonstick spray and lightly dust with flour.
2 Combine the flour, sugar, baking powder, salt, and baking soda in a large bowl. With a pastry blender, cut in the butter until the mixture is crumbly. Stir in the currants and caraway seeds. Add the buttermilk and stir with a wooden spoon just until the dry ingredients are moistened. Knead the mixture in the bowl just until it forms a dough, 5–6 times. Shape into a 6-inch circle and transfer to the baking sheet.
3 With a sharp knife, cut a ½-inch-deep X over the surface of the circle. Bake until golden brown and a toothpick inserted in the center comes out clean, 45–50 minutes. Let cool about 10 minutes and serve warm or cool completely on a rack. Cut into 12 wedges.

PER SERVING (1 wedge): 130 Cal, 2 g Fat, 1 g Sat Fat, 0 g Trans Fat, 6 mg Chol, 301 mg Sod, 25 g Carb, 1 g Fib, 3 g Prot, 41 mg Calc. ***POINTS*** value: ***3.***

GOOD IDEA This bread freezes beautifully, tightly wrapped in plastic wrap, up to 3 months, so make an extra loaf for unexpected guests if you're so inclined. It's also delicious toasted.

Banana-Strawberry Quick Bread

HANDS-ON PREP **20 MIN**
COOK **55 MIN**
SERVES **16**

- **2** cups all-purpose flour
- **2** teaspoons baking powder
- **½** teaspoon cinnamon
- **½** teaspoon salt
- **¼** teaspoon baking soda
- **¼** teaspoon ground nutmeg
- **2** very ripe medium bananas, mashed (about 1 cup)
- **2** large eggs
- **⅔** cup sugar
- **½** cup low-fat buttermilk
- **5** tablespoons canola oil
- **1** teaspoon vanilla extract
- **½** cup strawberry jam

1 Preheat the oven to 350°F. Spray a 4 x 8-inch loaf pan with nonstick spray and lightly dust with flour.

2 Combine the flour, baking powder, cinnamon, salt, baking soda, and nutmeg in a large bowl. Whisk together the bananas, eggs, sugar, buttermilk, oil, and vanilla in a medium bowl until smooth. Add the banana mixture to the flour mixture and stir until well blended. Transfer 3 tablespoons of the batter to a small bowl; set aside. Pour the remaining batter into the pan. Whisk together the jam and the reserved 3 tablespoons batter. Spoon the jam mixture lengthwise along the center of the batter, leaving a ½-inch border at each end of the pan.

3 Bake until a toothpick inserted in the center of the loaf comes out clean, 55–60 minutes. Let cool in the pan on a rack about 15 minutes. Remove from the pan and cool completely on the rack. Cut into 16 slices.

PER SERVING (1 slice): 180 Cal, 5 g Fat, 1 g Sat Fat, 0 g Trans Fat, 27 mg Chol, 156 mg Sod, 31 g Carb, 1 g Fib, 3 g Prot, 26 mg Calc. ***POINTS*** value: ***4.***

GOOD IDEA Got some extra ripe bananas? Just stick any unpeeled bananas in the freezer. Use them for fruit smoothies or, when you're in the mood, to bake another loaf of banana bread!

Old-Time Gingerbread

HANDS-ON PREP **15 MIN**
COOK **35 MIN**
SERVES **16**

- **1½ cups all-purpose flour**
- **2 teaspoons ground ginger**
- **1 teaspoon baking powder**
- **½ teaspoon baking soda**
- **½ teaspoon cinnamon**
- **¼ teaspoon ground nutmeg**
- **¼ teaspoon ground cloves**
- **¼ teaspoon salt**
- **6 tablespoons unsalted butter**
- **⅓ cup packed dark brown sugar**
- **½ cup molasses**
- **1 large egg**
- **½ cup boiling water**

1 Preheat the oven to 350°F. Spray a 4 x 8-inch loaf pan with nonstick spray and lightly dust with flour.

2 Combine the flour, ginger, baking powder, baking soda, cinnamon, nutmeg, cloves, and salt in a bowl. With an electric mixer on medium-high speed, beat the butter and brown sugar in a large bowl until fluffy, about 2 minutes. Beat in the molasses and egg until well combined. With the mixer on low speed, add the flour mixture until well blended. Beat in the boiling water. Pour the batter in the pan. Bake until a toothpick inserted in the center of the loaf comes out clean, 33–35 minutes. Let cool in the pan on a rack 5 minutes. Remove from the pan and serve warm or cool completely on the rack. Cut into 16 slices.

PER SERVING (1 slice): 131 Cal, 5 g Fat, 3 g Sat Fat, 0 g Trans Fat, 25 mg Chol, 110 mg Sod, 21 g Carb, 0 g Fib, 2 g Prot, 36 mg Calc. ***POINTS*** value: ***3.***

GOOD IDEA For an extravagant and rich-tasting dessert, top each slice of warm gingerbread with a ¼-cup scoop of fat-free vanilla ice cream and a sprinkling of cinnamon (the per-serving ***POINTS*** value will increase by 1).

Chocolate Angel Food Cake with Macerated Strawberries

HANDS-ON PREP **25 MIN**
COOK **35 MIN**
SERVES **12**

CAKE

- **1 cup cake flour**
- **⅓ cup unsweetened cocoa powder**
- **10 large egg whites, at room temperature**
- **1¼ cups sugar**
- **1 teaspoon cream of tartar**
- **¼ teaspoon salt**
- **2 teaspoons vanilla extract**

MACERATED STRAWBERRIES

- **2 pints fresh strawberries, hulled and sliced (about 6 cups)**
- **¼ cup sugar**
- **1 teaspoon grated orange zest**
- **¼ cup fresh orange juice**

1 To make the cake, preheat the oven to 350°F. Combine the cake flour and cocoa powder in a small bowl; sift twice.
2 With an electric mixer on medium speed, beat the egg whites in a large bowl until thick and foamy. Gradually sprinkle in the sugar, cream of tartar, and salt; continue beating until medium peaks form, 3–5 minutes.
3 Gently fold one-third of the flour mixture into the beaten whites with a rubber spatula until well combined; repeat 2 more times. Fold in the vanilla just until blended.
4 Pour the batter into a 10-inch tube pan. Tap the pan lightly on the counter to help remove any air bubbles; smooth the top of the batter. Bake until a toothpick inserted in the center comes out clean and the cake begins to pull away from the sides of the pan, 35–40 minutes. Invert onto a bottleneck or inverted metal funnel and cool completely. To loosen, run a knife around the sides of the pan and the center tube. Unmold the cake onto a serving plate.
5 Meanwhile, to make the macerated strawberries, combine all the ingredients in a large bowl. Refrigerate, stirring occasionally, until the sugar dissolves and the flavors are blended, about 1 hour or overnight. Serve with the cake.

PER SERVING (1/12 of cake with generous ¼ cup strawberries): 169 Cal, 1 g Fat, 0 g Sat Fat, 0 g Trans Fat, 0 mg Chol, 96 mg Sod, 38 g Carb, 2 g Fib, 4 g Prot, 14 mg Calc. ***POINTS*** value: ***3.***

GOOD IDEA This cake is wonderful as a leftover treat. Simply toast a slice in the oven or toaster oven until lightly crisped.

CARROT CAKE WITH CREAM
CHEESE FROSTING

Carrot Cake with Cream Cheese Frosting

HANDS-ON PREP **30 MIN**
COOK **30 MIN**
SERVES **24**

- **3½ cups all-purpose flour**
- **1 tablespoon pumpkin pie spice**
- **2 teaspoons baking powder**
- **1 teaspoon baking soda**
- **½ teaspoon salt**
- **3 large eggs**
- **1 cup plain fat-free yogurt**
- **1 cup unsweetened applesauce**
- **1 cup packed light brown sugar**
- **½ cup canola oil**
- **2 tablespoons grated orange zest**
- **1 tablespoon vanilla extract**
- **3 medium carrots, shredded (about 2 cups)**
- **1 cup golden raisins**
- **1 (8-ounce) package fat-free cream cheese**
- **3 ounces light cream cheese (Neufchâtel)**
- **1½ cups confectioners' sugar**

1 Preheat the oven to 375°F. Spray 2 (9-inch) round cake pans with nonstick spray and dust with flour.

2 Combine the flour, pumpkin pie spice, baking powder, baking soda, and salt in a medium bowl. With an electric mixer on high speed, beat the eggs, yogurt, applesauce, brown sugar, oil, 1 tablespoon of the orange zest, and the vanilla in a large bowl until blended. With the mixer on low speed, gradually add the flour mixture just until blended, 2–3 minutes. Stir in the carrots and raisins. Spread the batter evenly in the pans. Bake until a toothpick inserted in the center of each cake layer comes out clean, 30–35 minutes. Let cool in the pans on racks, 10 minutes. Remove from the pans and cool completely on the racks.

3 To make the frosting, with an electric mixer on high speed, beat the fat-free and light cream cheeses, the confectioners' sugar, and the remaining 1 tablespoon orange zest in a medium bowl until light and fluffy.

4 Place 1 cake layer on a serving plate. Spread the top with about ½ cup of the frosting, then cover with the remaining cake layer. Frost the top and sides of the cake with the remaining frosting.

PER SERVING (1/24 of cake): 233 Cal, 6 g Fat, 1 g Sat Fat, 0 g Trans Fat, 30 mg Chol, 225 mg Sod, 39 g Carb, 1 g Fib, 5 g Prot, 77 mg Calc. ***POINTS*** value: ***5.***

FOOD NOTE Carrot cake can easily become a zucchini cake by substituting 2 cups shredded zucchini for the carrots.

Apple Tart Tatin

HANDS-ON PREP **25 MIN**
COOK **1 HR 15 MIN**
SERVES **12**

- **1** **cup sugar**
- **3** **tablespoons water**
- **1** **teaspoon vanilla extract**
- **2** **teaspoons unsalted butter, diced**
- **10** **Golden Delicious apples (about 4 pounds), peeled and quartered**
- **1** **(7½-ounce) package refrigerated pie dough**

1 Combine the sugar, water, and vanilla in a 10½-inch cast iron skillet; dot with the butter. Starting at the edge of the skillet, arrange the apples in concentric circles on the sugar mixture, filling in the center with any remaining apples.

2 Set the skillet over medium-low heat and cook the apples, basting occasionally, until the sugar dissolves, the apples are tender, and the syrup becomes golden, 55–60 minutes. Remove the skillet from the heat and let the apple filling cool 5 minutes.

3 Meanwhile, preheat the oven to 425°F. On a lightly floured surface, roll out the dough to a 12-inch circle. Place the dough over the filling. Carefully tuck the edge of the dough along the inside of the skillet. Transfer the skillet to the oven and bake until the crust is golden, 18–20 minutes.

4 Remove the skillet from the oven; let cool about 10 minutes. Invert a large platter on top of the skillet. Quickly turn the skillet upside down to unmold the tart. Serve warm or at room temperature.

PER SERVING (1/12 of tart): 241 Cal, 6 g Fat, 2 g Sat Fat, 0 g Trans Fat, 5 mg Chol, 66 mg Sod, 49 g Carb, 3 g Fib, 1 g Prot, 7 mg Calc. ***POINTS*** value: ***5.***

PLAY IT SAFE When unmolding the tart from the hot skillet onto the serving platter, it's a good idea to wear oven mitts to protect your hands. If any apples stick to the skillet after unmolding, simply replace them on top of the tart with a spatula.

APPLE TART TATIN

PEAR CRISP

Pear Crisp

HANDS-ON PREP **20 MIN**
COOK **55 MIN**
SERVES **8**

- **½ cup + 2 tablespoons all-purpose flour**
- **½ cup quick-cooking or old-fashioned (not instant) rolled oats**
- **½ cup sugar**
- **1 teaspoon cinnamon**
- **½ teaspoon ground ginger**
- **⅛ teaspoon salt**
- **3 tablespoons unsalted butter, diced**
- **1 teaspoon water**
- **3 pounds pears, peeled and thinly sliced**
- **1 teaspoon vanilla extract**

1 Preheat the oven to 375°F. Spray a 7 x 11-inch baking dish with nonstick spray.

2 To make the topping, combine the ½ cup flour, the oats, ¼ cup of the sugar, ¼ teaspoon of the cinnamon, ¼ teaspoon of the ginger, and the salt in a medium bowl. Add the butter and pinch with your fingers to form coarse crumbs. Add the water and firmly press the mixture to form clumps.

3 To make the filling, combine the pears, the remaining ¼ cup sugar, the 2 tablespoons flour, the remaining ¾ teaspoon cinnamon and ¼ teaspoon ginger, and the vanilla in a large bowl; mix well. Transfer to the baking dish. Sprinkle the topping over the filling. Bake until the filling is bubbly and the topping is golden, 55–60 minutes. Serve warm or at room temperature.

PER SERVING (about ¾ cup): 182 Cal, 5 g Fat, 3 g Sat Fat, 0 g Trans Fat, 12 mg Chol, 40 mg Sod, 34 g Carb, 3 g Fib, 2 g Prot, 15 mg Calc. ***POINTS*** value: ***3.***

GOOD IDEA This crisp is just as delicious if you use Golden Delicious apples—and try substituting ground allspice for the ginger.

Cinnamon-Orange Rice Pudding

HANDS-ON PREP **10 MIN**
COOK **1 HR**
SERVES **6**

3 cups whole milk
¾ cup water
½ cup converted rice
1 (3-inch) cinnamon stick
½ teaspoon salt
⅓ cup sugar
⅓ cup golden raisins
1 teaspoon grated orange zest
¾ teaspoon vanilla extract
¼ teaspoon ground cinnamon

1 Combine 2 cups of the milk, the water, rice, cinnamon stick, and salt in a medium saucepan. Bring to a boil over medium-high heat. Reduce the heat and simmer, covered, until the liquid is almost absorbed, about 30 minutes.
2 Stir in the remaining 1 cup milk, the sugar, raisins, orange zest, and vanilla. Return the mixture to a simmer and cook, covered, stirring occasionally, until the rice is tender and the mixture is very creamy, about 25 minutes. Remove the pan from the heat; discard the cinnamon stick.
3 Divide the pudding among 6 bowls and sprinkle with the ground cinnamon. Serve warm or at room temperature.

PER SERVING (generous ⅓ cup): 204 Cal, 4 g Fat, 3 g Sat Fat, 0 g Trans Fat, 17 mg Chol, 256 mg Sod, 36 g Carb, 1 g Fib, 6 g Prot, 157 mg Calc. ***POINTS*** value: ***4.***

GOOD IDEA This rice pudding can be made up to 3 days ahead. Prepare as directed through step 2, then cover and refrigerate in an airtight container. Serve straight from the fridge, or to reheat, combine the pudding and ¼ cup fat-free milk in a medium saucepan. Cook over medium heat until warm, about 5 minutes. Either way, don't sprinkle the pudding with the ground cinnamon until you're ready to serve it.

Chocolate Cranberry Biscotti

HANDS-ON PREP **20 MIN**
COOK **35 MIN**
SERVES **20**

- **1½ cups all-purpose flour**
- **½ cup unsweetened cocoa powder**
- **2 teaspoons baking powder**
- **½ teaspoon baking soda**
- **¼ teaspoon salt**
- **¾ cup sugar**
- **2 large eggs**
- **2 tablespoons unsalted butter, melted**
- **1 teaspoon vanilla extract**
- **¾ cup sweetened dried cranberries**
- **1 ounce white chocolate**

1 Preheat the oven to 350°F. Spray a large baking sheet with nonstick spray.

2 Combine the flour, cocoa powder, baking powder, baking soda, and salt in a large bowl. With an electric mixer on medium speed, beat the sugar, eggs, melted butter, and vanilla in a medium bowl. On low speed, add the flour mixture to the egg mixture until well combined (the dough will be fairly dry). Add the cranberries, kneading the dough a few times in the bowl if necessary.

3 Sprinkle a work surface lightly with flour. Turn the dough onto the surface and divide in half. Working 1 piece at a time, roll the dough with the palms of your hands into a 15 x 1½-inch log. Place the log on the baking sheet. Repeat with remaining dough, placing the logs 2 inches apart. Bake until firm and a toothpick inserted into the center of each log comes out clean, about 15 minutes. With a wide spatula, carefully transfer the logs to a cutting board; let cool 10 minutes.

4 Meanwhile, reduce the oven temperature to 300°F. With a serrated knife, slice each log crosswise into 30 (½-inch-thick) slices. Place the slices 1 inch apart on the baking sheet. Bake until fairly dry, about 10 minutes on each side. Cool completely on a rack.

5 Place the white chocolate in a small microwavable bowl and microwave on High, stirring every 15 seconds, until melted and smooth, 45–60 seconds. Transfer the chocolate to a small zip-close plastic bag. Cut a tiny corner from the bag and decoratively pipe the chocolate over the cookies. Refrigerate or let stand in a cool place until the chocolate is firm.

Per serving (3 cookies): 108 Cal, 3 g Fat, 1 g Sat Fat, 0 g Trans Fat, 25 mg Chol, 102 mg Sod, 20 g Carb, 1 g Fib, 2 g Prot, 18 mg Calc. ***POINTS*** value: ***2.***

CHERRY FUDGE BROWNIES

Cherry Fudge Brownies

HANDS-ON PREP **15 MIN**
COOK **30 MIN**
SERVES **16**

- **3/4 cup all-purpose flour**
- **2/3 cup unsweetened cocoa powder**
- **1 teaspoon baking powder**
- **1/8 teaspoon salt**
- **1 cup granulated sugar**
- **1/4 cup butter, melted**
- **2 large eggs**
- **1 teaspoon vanilla extract**
- **1/2 teaspoon almond extract**
- **1/3 cup chopped dried cherries**
- **1/4 cup semisweet chocolate chips**
- **2 tablespoons confectioners' sugar (optional)**

1 Preheat the oven to 350°F. Spray an 8-inch square baking pan with nonstick spray.
2 Combine the flour, cocoa powder, baking powder, and salt in a large bowl. Combine the granulated sugar, melted butter, eggs, vanilla, and almond extract in another bowl. Stir the sugar mixture into the flour mixture just until blended. Fold in the cherries and chocolate chips.
3 Pour the batter into the pan and bake until a toothpick inserted in the center comes out almost clean, 28–32 minutes. Let cool in the pan on a rack 30 minutes. Cut into 16 bars and sprinkle with the confectioners' sugar through a fine sieve (if using). Serve warm or cool completely.

PER SERVING (1 bar): 141 Cal, 5 g Fat, 3 g Sat Fat, 0 g Trans Fat, 34 mg Chol, 86 mg Sod, 25 g Carb, 2 g Fib, 2 g Prot, 30 mg Calc. ***POINTS*** value: ***3.***

GOOD IDEA For a special dessert sundae, place a brownie in a bowl and top with a 1/4-cup scoop of fat-free frozen vanilla yogurt, 1/4 cup fat-free whipped topping, and a maraschino cherry (the per-serving ***POINTS*** value will increase by 2).

Coconut Macaroons

HANDS-ON PREP **20 MIN**
COOK **20 MIN**
SERVES **16**

- **1** (7-ounce) package shredded sweetened coconut
- **½** cup fat-free sweetened condensed milk
- **2** tablespoons all-purpose flour
- **½** teaspoon coconut extract
- **¼** teaspoon vanilla extract
- **2** egg whites
- **⅛** teaspoon salt

1 Preheat the oven to 325°F. Spray a large baking sheet with nonstick spray.
2 Combine the shredded coconut, condensed milk, flour, coconut extract, and vanilla in a bowl; mix well.
3 With an electric mixer on high speed, beat the egg whites and salt in a large bowl until stiff peaks form, 3–4 minutes. With a large rubber spatula, gently fold one-third of the beaten whites into the coconut mixture just until blended. Repeat 2 more times.
4 Drop the dough by rounded teaspoonfuls onto the baking sheet, 1 inch apart, making 32 cookies. Bake until lightly golden, 20–22 minutes. Cool on the baking sheet until the cookies are firm enough to remove from the baking sheet, about 20 minutes. Transfer the cookies with a spatula to racks to cool completely.

PER SERVING (2 cookies): 95 Cal, 4 g Fat, 4 g Sat Fat, 0 g Trans Fat, 1 mg Chol, 68 mg Sod, 13 g Carb, 1 g Fib, 2 g Prot, 30 mg Calc. ***POINTS*** value: ***2.***

GOOD IDEA If you don't have coconut extract, simply increase the amount of vanilla to ½ teaspoon.

Tropical Fruit Salad

HANDS-ON PREP **20 MIN**
COOK **5 MIN**
SERVES **6**

1 Heat a small skillet over medium heat. Add the coconut and cook, shaking occasionally, until lightly browned, 5–6 minutes; let cool.
2 Meanwhile, combine the remaining ingredients in a large bowl. Refrigerate until chilled and the flavors are blended, about 30 minutes. Divide the salad among 6 bowls; sprinkle each serving with 2 teaspoons of the coconut.

PER SERVING (1½ cups): 181 Cal, 2 g Fat, 1 g Sat Fat, 0 g Trans Fat, 0 mg Chol, 15 mg Sod, 43 g Carb, 6 g Fib, 2 g Prot, 48 mg Calc. ***POINTS*** value: ***3.***

GOOD IDEA To get a jumpstart on the prep and allow time for the fruit to give off their juices, prepare the dessert, and refrigerate covered, overnight—but don't add the bananas or the coconut garnish until just before serving.

- **¼ cup shredded sweetened coconut**
- **3 cups peeled and cubed fresh pineapple**
- **1 large mango, peeled, pitted, and cut into ¾-inch cubes**
- **1 pint fresh strawberries, hulled and quartered**
- **2 bananas, cut into 1-inch pieces**
- **2 kiwi fruit, peeled and cut into ¼-inch-thick slices**
- **2 oranges, peeled, halved, and cut into ¼-inch-thick slices**
- **¼ cup thinly sliced fresh basil**
- **3 tablespoons fresh orange juice**
- **3 tablespoons fresh lime juice**
- **1 tablespoon sugar**

Mango Sorbet

HANDS-ON PREP **20 MIN**
COOK **NONE**
SERVES **6**

- **3** **mangoes, peeled, pitted, and coarsely chopped**
- **¾** **cup sugar**
- **1** **teaspoon grated lime zest**
- **1** **teaspoon grated orange zest**
- **3** **tablespoons fresh lime juice**
- **3** **tablespoons fresh orange juice**

1 Lightly spray an 8-inch square baking dish with nonstick spray.
2 Puree the mangoes, sugar, lime zest, orange zest, lime juice, and orange juice in a food processor. Transfer the mixture to the baking dish and freeze until firm, about 2 hours.
3 Return the mixture to the food processor and process until smooth and creamy. Return the mixture to the baking dish and freeze until firm, about 1 hour.

PER SERVING (½ cup): 170 Cal, 0 g Fat, 0 g Sat Fat, 0 g Trans Fat, 0 mg Chol, 3 mg Sod, 44 g Carb, 2 g Fib, 1 g Prot, 13 mg Calc. ***POINTS*** value: ***3.***

FOOD NOTE You can keep a batch of this refreshing sorbet in the freezer up to 1 month. If the sorbet is frozen for more than an hour, let it soften at room temperature about 10 minutes before serving so it's easy to scoop.

MANGO SORBET;
CHOCOLATE CRANBERRY
BISCOTTI, PAGE 289

Roasted Pineapple with Cayenne and Allspice

HANDS-ON PREP **5 MIN**
COOK **15 MIN**
SERVES **4**

- **1 peeled and cored pineapple**
- **1½ teaspoons canola oil**
- **¼ teaspoon ground allspice**
- **⅛ teaspoon cayenne**
- **1 tablespoon fresh lime juice**

1 Preheat the oven to 500°F. Spray a large baking sheet with nonstick spray.
2 Cut the pineapple lengthwise into 16 thin wedges. Lightly brush both sides of each wedge with the oil; sprinkle with the allspice and cayenne.
3 Place the pineapple, curved side down, on the baking sheet. Roast until tender, about 12 minutes. Remove the pineapple from the oven; increase the oven temperature to broil. Brush the pineapple with the lime juice and broil 5 inches from the heat until lightly browned on the edges, 1–2 minutes. Serve warm or at room temperature.

PER SERVING (4 wedges): 75 Cal, 2 g Fat, 0 g Sat Fat, 0 g Trans Fat, 0 mg Chol, 1 mg Sod, 15 g Carb, 2 g Fib, 1 g Prot, 10 mg Calc. ***POINTS*** value: ***1.***

ZAP IT For a soothing dessert that's ready at a moment's notice, place the roasted pineapple in an airtight container and refrigerate up to 3 days. When ready to serve, microwave 4 wedges at a time on High until warm, 1–2 minutes.

Pear Crisp, page 287

Dry and Liquid Measurement Equivalents

If you are converting the recipes in this book to metric measurements, use the following chart as a guide.

TEASPOONS	TABLESPOONS	CUPS	FLUID OUNCES
3 teaspoons	1 tablespoon		½ fluid ounce
6 teaspoons	2 tablespoons	⅛ cup	1 fluid ounce
8 teaspoons	2 tablespoons plus 2 teaspoons	⅙ cup	
12 teaspoons	4 tablespoons	¼ cup	2 fluid ounces
15 teaspoons	5 tablespoons	⅓ cup minus 1 teaspoon	
16 teaspoons	5 tablespoons plus 1 teaspoon	⅓ cup	
18 teaspoons	6 tablespoons	¼ cup plus 2 tablespoons	3 fluid ounces
24 teaspoons	8 tablespoons	½ cup	4 fluid ounces
30 teaspoons	10 tablespoons	½ cup plus 2 tablespoons	5 fluid ounces
32 teaspoons	10 tablespoons plus 2 teaspoons	⅔ cup	
36 teaspoons	12 tablespoons	¾ cup	6 fluid ounces
42 teaspoons	14 tablespoons	1 cup minus 2 tablespoons	7 fluid ounces
45 teaspoons	15 tablespoons	1 cup minus 1 tablespoon	
48 teaspoons	16 tablespoons	1 cup	8 fluid ounces

OVEN TEMPERATURE			
250°F	120°C	400°F	200°C
275°F	140°C	425°F	220°C
300°F	150°C	450°F	230°C
325°F	160°C	475°F	250°C
350°F	180°C	500°F	260°C
375°F	190°C	525°F	270°C

NOTE: Measurement of less than ⅛ teaspoon is considered a dash or a pinch. Metric volume measurements are approximate.

VOLUME	
¼ teaspoon	1 milliliter
½ teaspoon	2 milliliters
1 teaspoon	5 milliliters
1 tablespoon	15 milliliters
2 tablespoons	30 milliliters
3 tablespoons	45 milliliters
¼ cup	60 milliliters
⅓ cup	80 milliliters
½ cup	120 milliliters
⅔ cup	160 milliliters
¾ cup	175 milliliters
1 cup	240 milliliters
1 quart	950 milliliters

LENGTH	
1 inch	25 millimeters
1 inch	2.5 centimeters

WEIGHT	
1 ounce	30 grams
¼ pound	120 grams
½ pound	240 grams
1 pound	480 grams

Recipe Index

C

H

I

J

K

L

Q

R

S

T

W

Z

POINTS value Recipe Index

0 *POINTS* value

1 *POINTS* value

2 *POINTS* value

3 *POINTS* value

4 *POINTS* value

5 *POINTS* value

6 ***POINTS*** value

7 ***POINTS*** value

8 ***POINTS*** value

Core Plan Recipe Index ☑

Make It Core Index ☑

Here's a list of **Flex Plan** recipes with directions to make them fit the **Core Plan**.

Notes